The Story of Nathaniel Fanning

FIGHTING SAILOR

The Story of Nathaniel Fanning

FIGHTING SAILOR

by Ralph Edgar Bailey

maps by James MacDonald

frontispiece by Franz Altschuler

William Morrow and Company
New York 1966

Also by the same author

Indian Fighter

To V.G.B.

MAPS

CONTENTS

The Story of Nathaniel Fanning
FIGHTING SAILOR

Chapter One
CHASED BY THE ENEMY

At the first crack of musket fire Gilbert Fanning looked up in startled concern from the cargo list he was checking. He could see widening puffs of smoke far out on Fisher's Island Sound. Abruptly he turned and sent the nearest of a dozen dock workers to fetch a telescope from the cabin of a little brig moored to the far side of the long pier in Stonington, Connecticut.

With the glass to one eye he could see a small sloop under full sail, closely pursued by what he knew to be a warship's longboat. Some of the British sailors were bending their back to their oars in what appeared to be a determined effort to overhaul the sloop. Several others took turns, as fast as they could reload, in firing their muskets at the fleeing craft.

Without a doubt the small sailing vessel was the one in which his oldest son, Nathaniel Fanning, and a younger brother, Edmund, were bringing back to Stonington six fat sheep from their grazing ground on Fisher's Island, across the Sound. The animals were the last of a small flock that would be sent from the supply base at this small Connecticut seaport town to Washington's Army in New Jersey.

Obviously the pursuing longboat had been sent out from the British frigate which earlier that morning had been reported hove to off nearby Watch Hill, at the entrance to the Sound. The sheep, if captured, would provide fresh meat for the frigate's officers and crew.

Not only was there now the imminent danger of losing the sheep, so badly needed by the Continental Army in this spring of 1778, but two of Gilbert Fanning's sons might be captured by the British. They even might be forced to serve against their countrymen aboard a king's ship.

Satisfied with his appraisal of the situation after a careful look through the sea glass, Fanning abruptly shoved the folding sections of the telescope together, set the brass-bound instrument down carefully on the upturned end of a barrel, then gave a low-toned order. It sent a youth running up the sloping hill that led to the village square to give the alarm.

With this swift move Gilbert Fanning knew he had done all that he could to help his sons. And even the help of the village could be of service only if the little sloop managed to escape and gain the shelter of Stonington Harbor. He turned back resolutely to the task of getting the brig loaded in all haste. Sacks and barrels of flour, parched corn, potatoes, dried beans, salt pork, smoked hams, slabs of cured bacon and dried beef soon must be started on the long and dangerous journey to Washington's Army in New Jersey. Gilbert Fanning's patriotic job as agent for Quartermaster-General Nathanael Greene's "commissary line" now had to come ahead of his deep and growing concern for his sons' safety. If Nathaniel and Edmund were to escape the British longboat's foraging detail, they must do so by their own courage and skill in seamanship, for no help could reach them in time from Stonington.

The meetinghouse bell almost at once began to clang out a sharp, insistent alarm, so different from the calm, deliberate tone of a Sunday morning that its message could not be mistaken by anyone within sound of its harshly metallic notes. Thus rung, the bell was the signal to the people of Stonington that again they were in danger from the enemy. Once before, on August 30, in 1775, soon after the battle was fought on Lexington Green in Massachusetts, the bell had summoned them when the British sloop of war *Rose*, commanded by Captain James Wallace, had bombarded the little seaport.

Still Gilbert Fanning continued to speed the loading of the brig. She must sail with the tide that night up Long Island Sound to Saybrook, at the mouth of the Connecticut River, where men would be waiting to transfer her cargo to flatboats. The boats would be poled some distance up the river, where goods and animals would be set ashore. Ox carts and horse-drawn vehicles would haul the provisions, and the cattle and sheep would be driven to the distant Hudson River and ferried over that broad stream. Once in New Jersey, the supplies would be sent down to Washington's camp.

General Greene had enlisted Gilbert Fanning as his agent in Stonington for the "commissary line" of the Continental Army. His task was to assemble and dispatch badly needed supplies. Provisions and livestock were sent to Stonington because from there it was only a short sail up Long Island Sound to the Connecticut River or, sometimes, further on to the shorter and more shallow Housatonic.

Nearly all transport in the American colonies was by sea, for the long haul overland by road was too costly, even in those rare instances when for a short distance it was possible. There were virtually none but rough roads, impassable in the winter snows and usually muddy quagmires after heavy rains in spring and fall. Instead, men and goods went by small coasting vessels.

With a British warship hovering in the near distance and her longboat chasing two of Gilbert Fanning's sons and their boatload of sheep, anything could happen. If the longboat's crew dared to pursue the Stonington sloop into the harbor and the townsfolk fired upon them—as they most certainly would if the boat came within musket range—and if the cannon were to blow up the longboat and its crew, the frigate was certain to retaliate by bombarding the town and its shipping.

This prospect made it imperative that Fanning complete the loading of the brig at once. She might have to sail ahead of time, before the warship could destroy her, along with the supplies. Gilbert Fanning had not disappointed George Washington or Nathanael Greene yet in delivering supplies, and he didn't intend to disappoint them now. So he forced himself to concentrate on his work. He ordered the cattle and sheep that were penned secretly behind a low wooded hill to be herded down to the pier and driven aboard. An onlooker almost might have thought that he was suddenly indifferent to the fate of his boys. This distinguished-looking man, neatly dressed in blue homespun with white ruffles at throat and wrists, appeared outwardly calm as he coolly directed the loading of the vessel. But he still was aware of sights and sounds from the outer harbor, and he glanced now and then at the progress of the race between the sloop and the longboat. There was a steely glint in his usually kindly eyes that told those who knew him well of his rising anger.

Gilbert Fanning nevertheless smiled grimly to himself as he thought how angry his two Tory brothers, Edmund and Thomas, would be if they could see him now. The brothers lived across the Sound on Long Island. Often they had berated him for his intense patriotism and his work in behalf of American independence. They were staunchly loyal to King George III. But much as his two Tory brothers hated

Gilbert Fanning's politics, they had not as yet set their British friends in New York against him. He'd give them credit for that. Or perhaps they had let him alone because he had been careful to ship most of the Continental Army's supplies to General Greene only on dark nights, when it would have been difficult for even sharp-eyed lookouts aboard British cruisers to spot the little brig.

Meanwhile, out on the Sound, Nathaniel Fanning himself tightly grasped the tiller of the little sloop with both hands. He lay flat on his back on the cockpit's hard wooden grating. The position was most uncomfortable, and already it seemed as though his arms would be pulled from their sockets because of the strain. Little beads of perspiration trickled down his forehead despite the early May morning chill.

Lying on his back with only his hands exposed was the only way he could think of to steer the sloop and at the same time find some measure of protection from the splatter of British musket balls from the pursuing longboat. Leaden pellets continued to cut holes in the mainsail as they had for the past quarter of an hour. Now and then one buried itself in the stout oak planks of the hull. He expected at any second that an unlucky shot might cut a halyard and send the mainsail billowing down onto the deck. Then the half dozen frightened, loudly bleating sheep penned securely forward indeed would fall prey to the British foraging crew. And perhaps both he and his brother Edmund would be impressed into the British Navy and forced to serve against their own people, like so many other Americans. This thought put new strength into Fanning's tired arms. He was coldly angry now and determined to outrace the pursuing enemy at whatever cost. If he could only gain the shelter of Stonington Harbor he would be safe, for he believed that the British longboat's crew would not dare to chase him right to the Fanning pier. But could he be sure of that?

Nathaniel Fanning's thick mop of reddish hair was wet now from salt spray that sluiced over the sloop's bow. His gray-blue eyes squinted aloft to the sail again as more musket balls slugged through the canvas. He turned a little to one side, changing position to ease the strain on his arms, then grinned at his younger brother. Already, at nine, Edmund was big for his age, and he had been to sea, off and on, almost ever since he had learned to swim. The freckle-faced younger Fanning grinned back at his twenty-three-year-old brother and snugged down into a more comfortable position, trying to escape some of the cold salt spray. He had his own job to do, tending the mainsheet, the stout rope that controlled the long sailboom.

The race between the sloop and the longboat dragged on. Now and then there came a hoarse-voiced shout from the young British midshipman in command of the longboat— "You rebels heave to while I come aboard!" Then, when there was no response, there would come another ragged scatter of musket fire and the sound of ripping canvas or the hard *plunk* of a musket ball imbedding itself in the stern. The sloop barrelled forward, cutting and riding the rising ground swell like a frightened gull and throwing a heavy curtain of thin spray with every pitch.

At last, after what seemed a long time, the brothers were conscious of the fact that the firing was easing off. There was a long interval with no shots. Perhaps Edmund Fanning could safely raise his head for a quick look astern. The boy ducked as a lone musket ball zinged into the thick oak planking a foot below the gunwhale, but he had seen enough and his face, as he turned to his elder brother, bore a wide grin. The freshening breeze that gave greater speed to the sloop had slowed the longboat. The tired crewmen could not hold their pace at the oars. The ship's boat was falling behind noticeably. In another minute the sloop would be out of musket range.

Again Nathaniel Fanning smiled at his brother. His smile was most engaging, especially when he was happy, and lighted up his somewhat thin, weather-tanned face, showing a set of white, even teeth. His thin nose was red now with the bite of the chilly air on the open water and the cold salt spray, but there was a twinkle in his gray-blue eyes. The brothers, without putting the thought into words, knew that each, despite the danger, thoroughly was enjoying the encounter with the enemy. This feeling wasn't something they talked about much, but outwitting and outrunning a British man-o'-war crew for a long time had been a favorite pastime along Fisher's Island Sound. Suddenly the sun felt warmer and the sloop glided gracefully and purposefully along a patch of light that was as brilliant as though the water had been sprinkled with billions of diamonds.

Soon the sloop was far enough out of musket range for the helmsman to ease himself up onto the stern thwart, from which more natural seat he could steer more easily. Nathaniel Fanning glanced ruefully aloft again at the shot holes in the taut canvas, then shrugged. No use to worry about what had happened to the sail. It was a shame, of course, for a new sail to be so badly shot up, but it could be mended. What really mattered was that, with the help of his brother, he had saved the sheep.

He put the helm up sharply, luffed, and brought the sloop about on the other tack as he set her racing into the calmer water of Stonington Harbor. As the outline of homes and the meetinghouse steeple etched themselves into the skyline, he felt a surge of pride and relief. The escape had indeed been a narrow one.

Lithe and slim, a wide smile of triumph on his face, Fanning stood up a little later, bracing his body to the pitch and roll of the vessel as he eased her smartly alongside his father's stone jetty. He always liked to make a dashing entry when he neared a mooring. His brother proudly displayed his expert seamanship by letting go the halyards at just the right second and caught the billowing mainsail in his arms as it slumped to the deck. The sloop lost way and was fended gently alongside the pier. The frightened sheep bleated in high-pitched protest at whatever fate awaited them.

First to grasp the bowline that young Edmund tossed ashore was Gilbert Fanning. Edmund sprang to lower the single jib sail, and then climbed grinning onto the stone jetty behind his older brother. Their father nodded a silent "Well done, boys" as their mother smiled her wordless relief at the safe return of her sons.

Now there came a loud and prolonged cheer from the big crowd of men, women, and children on the pier. Friends and neighbors surged forward to shake hands with the Fanning brothers, congratulating them for being the most recent Stonington sailormen to outwit the British Navy. But tight-lipped Gilbert Fanning was more interested at the moment in making certain that neither of his sons had been hit by enemy musket balls.

Only now did Nathaniel Fanning realize the significance of the muskets carried by so many men on the pier, and the grim-looking black cannon that stood on its high-wheeled carriage in seemingly defiant readiness at the end of the jetty. His fellow townsmen had been ready to defy the crew of the enemy longboat if they had dared to enter the harbor. Such an act on the part of the villagers would have meant the almost certain bombardment of the town, perhaps resulting in much loss of life, but that prospect had not deterred them.

Satisfied at last that his sons had not been hurt, and after giving more orders to speed up the loading, Gilbert Fanning led the way up the sloping hill toward home. They would be quite ready, after this good morning's work, to sit down to the hearty noonday meal that Huldah Fanning had prepared. She had been interrupted in the last minutes of preparation by the ringing of the alarm bell and the distant sound of firing, and had hurried down to the jetty.

Gilbert Fanning, as though suddenly remembering, stopped and, reaching into the back pocket of his long-tailed blue coat, drew out a letter bearing a big red wax seal. Silently he handed the missive to his eldest son and watched, with a smile and a merry twinkle in his eyes, for the reaction. Nathaniel Fanning, his pulses suddenly leaping with excited anticipation, quickly slit the wax seal with a long forefinger and hastily read the message. As he had hoped, it was a long-awaited letter from Captain William Denison, brought in on the southbound packet from Boston only this morning. Denison was one of the ablest privateersmen sailing out of any New England port, and his letter summoned Nathaniel Fanning to Boston to serve on his new brig, *Angelica.*

Chapter Two
THE YOUNG PRIVATEERSMAN

The fourth year of the American War for Independence
was beginning. Even some staunch patriots were discouraged, but not the men and women of Stonington, Connecticut. They were as determined as ever to sever political
ties with Great Britain.

Washington's little Continental Army—a few thoroughly
trained, disciplined "regulars" who were in the fight "for the
duration"—was in a hidden camp somewhere in the wilds of
New Jersey. The Continental Army was waiting a chance to
pounce upon Sir Henry Clinton, the new British commander in New York. He had succeeded General Sir William Howe as the chief of King George's officers in North
America.

Although the war was not going well, so far as results were concerned, there were some bright spots for the Americans. Washington's Army had all but starved and frozen to death during the recent terrible winter encampment at Valley Forge, twenty miles outside of Philadelphia, but his ragged Continentals had held the British penned down in Philadelphia. The enemy had not dared to attack at Valley Forge because Washington had chosen a highly strategic position for his winter camp. Now the Continentals were ready to march again.

A Northern Army under General Horatio Gates had won a smashing victory over Gentleman Johnny Burgoyne at Saratoga, New York, the previous fall. Burgoyne's defeat saved the colonies from the danger of being split down the middle, for the Americans still held the vital line of the Hudson River above West Point. The British had been outmaneuvered at every turn in the North. Now they had been forced to plan for a campaign to crush the South. They still held New York as their headquarters in North America and their main base of supplies and troops from overseas only because Washington did not feel that his Army was strong enough to attack.

On the American side, as always, there was a dangerous need for men, money, and supplies this spring of 1778. The great victory over the British at Saratoga and the diplomatic skill of Doctor Benjamin Franklin at the French court at Versailles had been of tremendous value to the American colonies. As a result, King Louis XVI of France, who wanted an excuse to attack British overseas shipping anyway, had dispatched warships and troops to America to help the "rebels," and he had supplied money from the royal treasury to buy war supplies.

Enemy cruisers ranged the Atlantic seaboard like sharp-nosed terriers watching at ratholes through which American privateers and merchant ships might bring in supplies to help Washington's Army. Enemy warships were nowhere more numerous or more vigilant than in the waters of Long Island Sound.

Privateering had become a way of life for many Americans during the three years since the first shot of the war had been fired in the spring of 1775. It was a way of life that often proved highly profitable to those engaged in it. But, more important, privateering helped to supply Washington's Army with badly needed food, clothing, and money for the purchase abroad of gunpowder and ammunition for cannon and muskets. Only a very small amount of gunpowder was manufactured in America. Sometimes Washington's Army had only enough for a few rounds per man and almost none for their cannon.

Because the struggling American colonies had few re-sources and little money, they barely were able to build and equip more than a few war vessels as a part of a regular Navy. These ships usually were smaller than most of the king's ships they fought, and many of them were greatly outgunned, both in the number of cannon and in the size of the shot their guns could fire at the enemy.

Despite these handicaps, American privateers were playing a vitally important role in the war. They served, as the name implied, as an auxiliary to the small American Navy. Privateersmen held commissions from either Congress or a state government, authorizing them to capture enemy ships on the high seas and bring them into port. An American admiralty court then set a value on ship and cargo and the prize was sold to the highest bidder. The money was distributed to the owners of the privateer and to the officers and crew, who worked on shares. Some of the badly needed supplies, which could be had in no other way, ultimately found a place in the stores of the quartermaster general of Washington's Army.

Equally important, from a military point of view, was the fact that every ship captured by an American privateersman weakened by just so much the commerce of Great Britain, upon which her people depended for a living. After a while, despite the extremely heavy losses in the American privateer fleet, the fact that so many enemy vessels were captured also helped to some extent to weaken the British will to fight.

Almost every port along the Atlantic coast sent out privateers, most of which were built in local shipyards. Some of the privateers were highly successful in capturing enemy prizes with rich cargoes; others met with only indifferent success. Much depended on the skipper and how his luck ran.

Some privateers were captured or sunk by British warships or enemy privateers. There was no guarantee when a man sailed on such a venture that he would win big prize money. He was taking a chance that he might lose his life or that he might be captured by the enemy and either imprisoned or forced to serve in the king's Navy.

Even General Greene, who, as Washington's quartermaster, relied heavily on the heroic operations of the privateersmen, had found that success did not come with every cruise. His brothers in Rhode Island had invested money for him in several privateering ventures, but all the ships were captured and Greene lost all of the money he put into them.

Portland, Boston, Salem, Newburyport, Providence, Newport, Stonington, New London, New York, Philadelphia, and many ports along the Southern coast had sent out privateers.

Everyone along the coast who was close to privateering or in otherwise supplying Washington's Army with the sinews of war knew that a private trading company had been set up for the special use of Americans on the island of Saint Eustatius, or Statia in the lingo of foreign traders, in the West Indies. At Statia one could buy or trade almost anything, and fast American ships took on cargoes of gunpowder, cannon balls, muskets, pigs of lead to be melted and cast in molds as musket balls, canvas for tents and sails, and other war supplies. Often these fast ships ran such contraband of war into American ports under the very nose of patrolling British cruisers. Sometimes an American blockade runner was captured—now and then even before she barely had cleared Statia. But more often the ships successfully ran the blockade. And some of the blockade runners sailed under neutral flags, taking on cargoes of war supplies for America in French, Spanish, or Dutch ports.

What the world did not know at that time was that the secret trading firm of Hortalez and Company had been set up on the island of Statia by the kings of France and Spain. The island was controlled by the Dutch, who were supposed to be neutral in the war, and anyone could trade there. The company had been established largely through the efforts of Benjamin Franklin. He was the brains behind most of the important American diplomatic moves. Indeed, Franklin and Washington early in the war had recognized the vital role that shipping must play in the struggle.

The Fannings, like others interested in supplying the American Army, may have suspected the setup on Statia, but they probably were content to be doing their bit to help the cause without asking too many questions. What counted was success in running the British blockade. If, in the process, they succeeded in making a profit as well, they would be even more content.

Nathaniel Fanning had sailed twice before on successful privateering cruises. Now he was eager to undertake another such venture, either off the New England coast or to the West Indies, where the prizes, and the profits, were likely to

be even richer. New York, under the stern command of Sir
Henry Clinton, was closed more tightly than ever to American ships. Even before Clinton took over command from
Howe, New York had been cut off from the rebels, for Howe
had driven Washington's ragged little Army from Long Island and Manhattan in 1776. The Americans barely had escaped over the Harlem River to Harlem Heights. From
thence, after a battle, they crossed the Hudson River in a
masterly retreat into New Jersey. So now only Salem and
Boston, for the most part, were sending out privateers. Newport, under blockade by Admiral Howe, was more or less shut
off along with Providence, twenty miles up Narragansett Bay.
Boston at the moment seemed the only port where an eager
young man could get to sea again as a privateersman.

So Nathaniel Fanning had sought in Boston for a chance
to renew the kind of adventure he liked best and the job for
which he felt himself best trained to serve the American
cause. The Stonington Fannings had been outspoken from
the first in declaring for complete independence, a fact well
known along the seacoast towns in Massachusetts. The letter
from Boston was in reply to one Fanning had written some
time before to Captain Denison, an old friend of his father.

The Boston skipper was fitting out a new eighteen-gun
brig, the *Angelica*, as a privateer. Nathaniel Fanning could
have the job of prizemaster. In this berth he would take
command of a captured ship and sail or fight her into port.

Chapter Three
CAPTURED

shrouded the Atlantic early on the morning of
ter a night of calm, but a faint breeze had begun to
the southwest. Soon, if the wind held, the murk

had the watch and, as he stood beside the helms-
he brig's quarterdeck, his eyes strained to pierce the
of mist. The little ship was being held to slow
er fore and main topsails and a single jib, so she
making way in this hour before sunrise.

lly the mist began to thin out, and suddenly he
hat he was staring at what seemed to be a dark
yer than the fog bank, only a few hundred feet to
ff the larboard, or port, beam. He knew it must be

Daring seamanship and ingenuity were required of a prizemaster and Denison thought he had the right man for the
job.

But to be sure of reaching Boston in time Prizemaster
Fanning had to sail that very night with the tide on a packet
boat "down to Boston."

He gave little thought to the danger, even in face of the
fact that more privateersmen were being lost every day. The
British were determined to crush the Americans on the sea as
well as on the land. He felt just a twinge of regret at parting
from Betty Smith, the brown-haired neighbor girl who already had his deepening affection. Betty was going on fifteen,
and he couldn't think of asking her to marry him for yet
another year, at least, although some girls did marry at such
an early age. Betty was attractive, with laughing brown eyes
and a sunny disposition, and she had caught the eye of more
than one youth in Stonington. Nathaniel Fanning had dared
to hope for some time that she might prefer him a little more
than the others, but he couldn't be sure. Anyway, fighting
the war came first. That was his duty and this was his chance.
Besides, he couldn't yet support a wife. Perhaps on the cruise
out of Boston he might earn enough prize money to buy a
part interest in a small vessel and take command as captain.
There was little chance of doing so if he enlisted in the small
American Navy, much as the naval service appealed to him.
But as a privateersman he not only could fight for his country, he could hope, with a great deal of luck, both to stay

alive and to make good prize money. Youth is a time of dreams, and he had plenty of them.

So absorbed was he with plans for the future that he scarcely touched the appetizing meal of sizzling, browned roast pork with rich brown gravy, boiled potatoes, and boiled onions mixed with carrots, freshly baked pie made from some of the last of the winter apples, and scalding hot tea. There would be little for him to pack, he reflected—just a few extra clothes and his long-bladed sea knife. He realized with something approaching excitement that within a few hours he would be gone with the tide for Boston.

The run "down to Boston" involved little real danger. Sailors always spoke of it as "down" to Boston, because the prevailing winds usually flowed from some quarter in the south to the north, making it possible for a ship to sail "with the wind," or down wind when going north to Boston. The run back to Stonington always was "up," because then one had to take the wind on the quarter.

The little unarmed packet schooner made the run to Boston in record time, thanks chiefly to a favorable wind and the fact that few British cruisers happened at the moment to be prowling on her course. Her captain easily evaded the few war vessels he did sight.

Captain Denison proved to be a big, raw-boned, weather-bronzed, smooth-shaven man of few words and a booming voice. He had a good-natured look in his dark eyes, despite the firm set of his jaw. A man instinctively knew that here

was a skipper who would consideration he could to hi would insist upon running discipline. That way of saili wanted. He liked Captain Den

The new brig was a trim guessed that she was fast, too eighteen guns—eight small-b bore gun forward, with a ster trim and tidy little fighting craf

The *Angelica* sailed from 1778. For five days she prowl by British merchant vessels Philadelphia, and Halifax an enemy sail was sighted. Fan cheated.

Heavy
May 3
stir fro
would

Fan
man o
thick
speed
barely

Gr
realiz
objec
the le

another vessel, and in these dangerous wartime waters he had to consider that any strange ship was an enemy. This moment, at last, was the spine-tingling one for which he had been waiting these past five days! But for all his quick excitement and pounding pulse he reacted as calmly as though the brig and every man aboard had not suddenly been placed in grave danger.

Fanning's instinct and training enabled him to make a quick decision in an emergency. Stonington men, or any men who followed the sea, were likely to react that way, because years of sailing in all kinds of weather had taught them the necessity for prompt action, just to stay alive.

He sent the helmsman sprinting silently aft to awaken Captain Denison, who was asleep in his little stern cabin. Then the man was to waken members of the off watch forward. And before the skipper came running to the quarterdeck, buttoning his sea trousers as he ran, two other men of Fanning's watch had been ordered forward to set a second jib to give the brig more speed.

Captain Denison understood the situation at once. He pointed a long, bony finger at the lines of the big ship now rapidly taking shape off to larboard. He knew quite as well as his prizemaster that America had no naval ship as big as the one that loomed through the lifting murk. His dark eyes squinted for another long look at the stranger and his quick concern was evident. The towering bulk had to be a Britisher, probably nothing less than a seventy-four gun ship of the line. Fanning realized that he had sailed the *Angelica* right into a trap, and he voiced the thought, his tone carrying the self-disgust he felt. Captain Denison laid a quick, reassuring hand on his shoulder. The fog was so thick, he said, that it was lucky the Britisher hadn't rammed the brig.

Captain Denison rapped out quick, low-toned orders that sent sailors scampering up the ratlines to set fore and main sails. If the freshening breeze held and the fog didn't lift too fast, the *Angelica* might outrun the enemy. Already, thanks to the extra jib Prizemaster Fanning had ordered set, the brig noticeably was picking up speed.

But scarcely had Captain Denison given the order for more sail than there came a sharp hail across the water: "Ahoy! What ship is that?"

Captain Denison shrugged, but not quite in resignation, although both he and Prizemaster Fanning knew he must at once reply to the challenge. The brig was too close to the warship's guns for him to ignore the order to identify himself. Now, in the lifting fog, the towering hulk of the king's ship stood out more clearly. She was, indeed, a powerful ship of the line, flying British colors.

A cannon spoke from the stranger. The heavy ball of a bow chaser splashed fifty feet to the larboard of the *Angelica*. It had been fired intentionally short, but it was meant as a blunt warning for the brig to heave to at once. She must back her sails and stand by to await inspection. Captain Denison delayed as long as he dared, but the Britisher was at even closer range now and could sink him at will. Still, a bluff was worth trying.

Captain Denison cupped his hands and called, "This is His Majesty's ship *Neptune*, cruising off the New England coast as a privateer." Possibly such a reply might satisfy the British, even if not for long. There *were* British privateersmen in these waters, most of them sailed by Tory skippers whose loyalty was to King George.

Nathaniel Fanning could see the tall figure of an officer on the horse block, a raised platform abreast the warship's quarterdeck. This platform projected over the side of the vessel and from such a vantage point the officer of the deck had a clearer view of what went on below.

The Englishman called through his speaking trumpet, "Heave to, *Neptune*, while I send a boat over to inspect your papers!"

Captain Denison shrugged in resignation. If there had been even the slightest chance of getting away he would have taken it. The *Angelica* could make better time in this light wind than the heavy British seventy-four, but the fog had lifted too soon for him to gain this advantage. It would be senseless to engage the far heavier ship. He would be pitting his eighteen small-bore guns against the other's seventy-four big cannon. And even the brig's fore-and-aft Long Toms wouldn't be of much use in that kind of battle. Such an encounter would result in great loss of life, and the *Angelica* could not hope to win. But it was maddening to think that, only five days out of Boston with a new ship, she had been trapped with no chance either to fight or to run!

There was light enough now, with the sun shining faintly through the rapidly lifting fog, so that Fanning clearly could make out the quarterdeck of the British warship. He pointed in some excitement to a red-coated man who had joined the officer of the deck on the horse block. The officer wore the scarlet tunic, gold epaulets, white knee breeches, black, polished boots, and black cocked hat of the British Army.

Captain Denison squinted in the direction of his prizemaster's pointing finger, then commented, "That's Sir William Howe!"

Fanning realized at once, with something of a sinking sensation at the pit of his stomach, what the captain's statement could mean. Almost everyone knew that the king had relieved Sir William of his command in North America and ordered Sir Henry Clinton to replace him. Howe was on his way back to England in a kind of military disgrace, although he had, in fact, asked to be sent home. But he faced a court of inquiry for his conduct of the war, which had dragged on for more than three years without definite results. The warship that had overhauled the *Angelica* could be none other than the powerful ship of the line *Andromeda*. It was known that Sir William was to return home aboard her. What this unfortunate circumstance could mean to the officers and crew of the *Angelica* was something Fanning and all the others aboard the privateer had to think about at once. For it was said that Sir William, who for years had been an ardent champion of the rights of the American rebels, now hated them just as intensely. This change had come about because the general and his brother, Admiral Lord Howe, had failed to win American support for a peace commission. Both the Howes now felt that the colonials were ungrateful. But the American colonies had gone too far in their war for independence for such a plan to succeed without a royal guarantee that all demands would be met. And since King George III had refused to give such a guarantee of complete independence, the attempted negotiations for peace had fallen through. There was a growing anti-war party in Britain, to be sure, but it would be a long time before its champions could make much headway against the stubborn king and the warlike ministry of Frederick, Lord North.

Captain Denison had expected only minimum danger from British patrol craft when he sailed from Boston May 26. He knew that Admiral Lord Howe's powerful blockading fleet was cruising off the coast. But Admiral Howe was not likely to waste much time on a comparatively small vessel, even if he suspected her of being a privateer. He had more important work to do at the moment. Apparently Captain Denison had forgotten the *Andromeda*, or had hoped to elude her if she were encountered.

The captain strode to the near rail of the *Angelica* and ordered his boatswain to pipe aboard the British lieutenant as the *Andromeda's* longboat came alongside.

How would Sir William vent his spleen on the brig's officers and crew? Would he order them to be taken back to New York and jailed aboard one of the horrible British prison hulks? Everyone knew these dismantled and discarded old warships deserved their name—floating hell—and that American prisoners died aboard them like flies because of disease, poor food, little water, and lack of sufficient air in their foul-smelling below-deck quarters. Or would Sir William decide to take his prisoners to England and send them to one of the big naval prisons? Some of these wartime prisons were said to be fully as horrible as the floating death hulks in New York Harbor.

Chapter Four
MUTINY

The young British naval lieutenant came over the side of the *Angelica* with great dignity and self-importance. He was most correct, but he wasted no time. Would Captain Denison be so kind as to show him the ship's papers? Captain Denison returned the officer's salute and escorted him aft to his cabin. Within minutes they returned to the deck and the lieutenant reported to the warship by speaking trumpet. Soon two boatloads of sailors and marines pulled smartly for the brig.

When, a little later, Captain Denison went aboard the *Andromeda* as a prisoner, Sir William Howe ignored his salute and curtly told the master of the *Angelica* that since Denison and his men were little better than pirates, they

would be treated with something less than the normal cour-
tesy given to prisoners of war. The brig's officers would be
free on deck parole if they promised not to try to escape; the
crewmen would be confined below. The *Angelica* would be
sunk by gunfire.

Armed marines prodded the men and boys of the crew
down a forward companion ladder to the next to the lowest
deck, and the hatch was closed and secured. Down there,
almost at bilge level, the only air was that which came into
the compartment when the bulkhead hatch was opened.
Once a day, in good weather, the men would be escorted
under guard to the open deck for an hour of fresh air and
sunshine. The rest of the time, for the thirty days or more
required for the voyage to England, they would eat, sleep,
and get what little exercise they could in the almost complete darkness of their cramped quarters. Already, within the
first hour, the heat was terrific and the lack of oxygen was
almost unbearable. Fanning, despite his buoyant good
health, breathed with difficulty. How some of the other men
would manage to live four or five weeks under such conditions he didn't know. Even worse, he had heard Sir William
tell Captain Denison that when they reached England he
would have all the prisoners put on trial in a naval court as
pirates. If found guilty, as they almost certainly would be,
they would be hanged.

Within twenty-four hours the heat in the below-deck
prison became so intense that most of the men took off their

clothes. But even then they perspired so freely that they were dripping wet. A bowlful of slop that was called stew was served to them twice a day, with several buckets of water to be divided among them.

Such conditions could not be tolerated indefinitely. Some of the men were certain to sicken. Others were sure to die before they reached England. Whatever the danger there might be from dying later at the end of a hangman's noose, their present problem was to stay alive during the voyage. And this required prompt and desperate measures.

Always aboard a British man-o'-war there were numerous rebellious crewmen. Perhaps aboard the *Andromeda* there were men who had been impressed into the British naval service against their will by a press gang. These press gangs regularly were sent out by the British when in port to round up enough men to fill a ship's crew. The press gangs roamed the waterfront and often drugged men in a grog shop or deliberately kidnapped them on dark streets at night. Once aboard ship they were forced to do what they were told or face a brutal flogging with a bull whip, a long leather thong with lead at the tip, or the cat-o'-nine tails, a nine-pronged whip of knotted cord. Sometimes men died under such torture. The more hardy of such men almost invariably joined a plot to mutiny against their often cruel officers.

The surgeon of the *Angelica*, who ranked as an officer, had the freedom of the deck under parole. The next time he came below to check on the brig's crewmen, as Captain

Denison insisted he should, Fanning outlined to him a daring plan for a fight for freedom. If the surgeon could persuade mutinous members of the *Andromeda's* crew to smuggle down knives, cutlasses, and pistols, the American prisoners might be able to overpower the guard at night, creep up the companion ladder, and overcome the deck watch. Then, with the help of their own officers, who would break deck parole and join the mutiny, and aided by the mutinous British seamen, they might capture the ship—and Sir William Howe! What a prize he would be to sail back with to Boston harbor!

The plot was carefully planned for nine bells on the night of June 3. Knives, several cutlasses, and a few pistols were smuggled down to the prisoners, along with a big supply of belaying pins. These long wooden pins, used to secure the ship's ropes, made wicked weapons. Even extra powder and ball for the pistols were provided by the plotters among the British crew. These men were serving aboard the *Andromeda* against their will, and they were anxious to make a bid for freedom. Some of them, if they had the chance, would join the Americans at sea in fighting their own country, so deep was their bitterness.

Next morning, after another meal of so-called stew, Fanning, along with the other prisoners, was escorted by armed marines to the waist of the upper gun deck for an hour of sunshine and fresh air. The prisoners were allowed to exercise or amuse themselves in any way they chose, but they were herded into a narrow area so as not to interfere with the running of the ship. Fanning noticed with growing confidence the sly winks and the occasional quick, friendly grins that came from various members of the British crew when their officers were not watching. These men were part of the conspiracy.

An hour was a pitifully short time to spend on deck on a fair day in the sunshine and fresh air, Fanning thought, when one knew that at the end of the period he must return to the foul-smelling hole near the bottom of the ship. All too soon the boatswain's whistle blew. It was the signal for the prisoners to be herded back down into their black, ill-ventilated dungeon.

"Where's Spencer?" Fanning suddenly asked, as he joined the single line of prisoners who were awaiting the signal to begin the climb back down onto the prison deck. Spencer was Captain Denison's clerk. He was a surly fellow and not at all liked by the others, but he was a good penman and therefore useful to the captain. Fanning looked around hurriedly for Spencer with a sudden unexplainable foreboding. Then he spotted the man. Spencer was on the quarterdeck, talking earnestly with Sir William Howe!

"What in the world—" Fanning started to say aloud to himself, when there came a sharp blare of a trumpet and marines began popping out from behind masts and deck housing, muskets at the ready.

"Arrest those prisoners!" bawled Sir William from the

quarterdeck. "They plan to lead a mutiny! Take them below
and secure the hatches! Double the guard!"

Spencer, of course, did not accompany the men whom the
marines, at bayonet point, thrust roughly down the companion ladder.

"The traitor!" was all Fanning could say. He felt as
though the end of the world had come. Back to that foul hole
and continued darkness—for how many weeks? And now the
prisoners faced charges of attempting to escape as well as
being pirates and rebels against the king. On mutiny charges
alone they could be hanged.

The marine guards seized the cutlasses, pistols, and knives
that had been left only partly concealed by the extra clothing
in the prison hold. There would be no chance now to overpower the watch. Despair took over the imprisoned crewmen
and Fanning could feel this reaction among the men. The
foul air of the below-deck dungeon itself seemed to reek of
the low spirits that the plot's failure had brought on. For
some time the prisoners were silent, and most of them tried
to get what uneasy rest they could.

After a while Fanning himself dozed off, and when he
awoke he could not tell whether it was day or night because
the deck hatch had been so tightly secured that it closed out
all light. He stretched his legs as far as he could for he felt
cramped. Then he raised his arms as far above his head as he
could. Suddenly his whole body tingled with excitement.
One hand had grasped what he knew to be the handle of a

knife. Doubtless it was a weapon the marines had overlooked when they had searched the prisoners' quarters. But Fanning's excitement subsided as quickly as it came. Of what use could a single knife be when they were securely locked up several decks below the main gun deck of the *Andromeda*?

Fanning pulled the knife toward him and idly began to pick with it at the deck planking. He had noticed, as had several of the others, that the boards were damp. Indeed, the moisture was one of the reasons for their discomfort. He guessed that this compartment had been used to store wine for the officers' mess and rum for the crew. In handling the liquid some of it had spilled on the planking. And there was the possibility, too, that in a rough passage a cask or two had broken open, the contents quickly being absorbed by the wood. This dampness would have a tendency to cause rot. Sea water also could have seeped into the compartment at times. If so, he could understand why it was so easy to dig out small chips of wood.

At first he had no plan; he merely idly chipped away with the point of the blade. Then slowly an idea began to form. Suppose the wood were so rotten and so thin that he could dig through to the deck below? What might be found there? Possibly a way of escape by surprising the guard who would not be looking for them on that deck level? Such an idea was fantastic, but there was nothing else for him to do and he continued to dig into the deck planking. Quite a pile of chips had accumulated by the time the idea jelled.

Then, fired by the very boldness of his plan, he told his companions of his find and of his experiment. He led them in a thorough search that turned up two more knives the marines had overlooked. The men eagerly took turns digging with a knife point, hiding the chips beneath discarded clothing. Fanning cautioned them to keep digging within a circle eighteen inches in diameter, which he had measured as well as he could in the dark by raising splinters to serve as markers. Hour after hour the digging continued as excitement mounted among the prisoners. There was no fear of interruption until the guard came with the next meal, and then they would have plenty of warning.

It was past four bells—six o'clock—when the evening meal of unpalatable slop arrived in the flickering light of a single candle-lit lantern and the guards saw nothing out of order in the crowded compartment. Soon they pulled up the ladder, refastened the hatch cover, and the prisoners fell to at the big iron pots of stew. The concoction was only lukewarm and they were glad because they had no spoons and were obliged to dip their cupped hands into the mess. In the darkness this way of eating was awkward and resulted in a good deal of waste, and the mess they made by spilling the stew on deck added to their discomfort. What was even worse, the guards had left only about a half pint of water for each man. They could drink it or use it for washing, but there wasn't enough water for both.

Quickly the sorry meal was finished, down to the last drop

and morsel in the big pots. When men are hungry enough they will eat anything, even the unsavory mess that Sir William had ordered cooked for his hated American prisoners. Fanning wished the general could be forced to eat the stuff himself, in pitch blackness and unclothed, too, with almost no air to breathe. And then let him wash the meal down with a few stingy mouthfuls of stale water. The general, however, was dining in his splendidly appointed cabin aft, with a bottle of fine old Madeira wine to wash down a savory meal. Somewhere aboard the ship were stored the fine smoke-cured hams, the bacon, beans, rice, and other edibles served specially for the general and the ship's captain, together with a selection of other wines. If the eighteen-inch hole through this planking only could lead to such a cache as that! But, of course, such a prize was almost unthinkable. The men of the *Angelica* were not likely to have such luck.

Chapter Five
SIR WILLIAM'S LOCKER

When the last plank was cut through Fanning lowered himself gingerly through the narrow hole. He found himself on a deck where great casks of water were stored. They served the officers and crew for drinking and cooking purposes. For washing they used sea water, drawn in wooden buckets over the side. At least, with this discovery, there now would be enough water for the prisoners, if they were not interrupted.

Success in finding this vital supply of water led Fanning to speculate what might be concealed behind the forward bulkhead. The men willingly took turns, at his suggestion, chipping a hole through the bulkhead wall. The work was hard, for the wood was tough, seasoned oak, and it had not begun to rot as had the deck planking. One had to be careful, too, and use only the tip of the knife blade in order not to take a chance on breaking the point.

Of course, there was the danger that Sir William might order the compartment thoroughly searched again at any time, but that was a chance they had to take. After three days and nights of laborious digging the men chipped through to the next compartment. Quickly Fanning wedged through the narrow opening and by feeling around in the pitch darkness soon discovered that, as he had hoped, it was filled with boxes, bales, and sacks of goods, with casks that surely contained wine. Moreover, most of the supply was at their end of the storage compartment, so that whatever pilfering they might do was not likely to be discovered right away. If some food and wine were missed later on in the voyage, the loss probably would be laid to thieving crewmen.

This prize was even richer than Fanning had dared to expect. There were smoked hams, slabs of smoked bacon, beef, barrels of dried peas and beans, flour—which would be of little use since it could not be cooked—and hampers filled with bottles of Madeira wine. He knew, even in the darkness, that it was Madeira by the shape of the bottles. All these supplies had been especially shipped for Sir William's table on the voyage. What was left he would take home. Doubtless most had been stolen from the Americans in one way or another, or bought at forced sale at a low price.

For the remainder of the voyage the prisoners lived well,

but they had to be careful. They had to force themselves to
continue eating the stew in the big iron pots, but they used
the stale water for washing. The peas and beans were soaked
in some of the water from the casks and after a few hours the
dried vegetables were soft enough to eat without cooking.
For this purpose they had to wheedle the guards into leaving
one of the pots each time after a meal. The ham and bacon
were sliced with the knives that had been used to dig
through the bulkhead. The meat had to be eaten raw, but it
provided good nourishment. Fanning warned the men that
they must voluntarily ration the amount of wine they drank
strictly. They could not afford to have even one man become
intoxicated, for if he did, he almost certainly would lead to
discovery of their secret.

When the *Andromeda* dropped anchor off Plymouth, England, on June 30, 1778, Sir William still had not discovered
that his private larder had been raided by the men he had
locked up as ordinary pirates.

Whatever plans the general may have had for putting his
prisoners before a military or naval court to be tried as
pirates came to nothing. Instead, they were transferred at
once to Forton Prison in Gosport, near Falmouth, to await
an exchange of prisoners by the French.

Fanning soon learned that there was no chance to escape
from Forton Prison. Fierce dogs, in addition to the regular
armed guards, patrolled the area outside the high walls.
Peasants, who owned the dogs, were offered a standing re-

ward of five pounds sterling, about twenty-five dollars in modern American money, for the capture of an escaped American prisoner. For a French prisoner the reward was only half a guinea, about one tenth as much as for an American.

Nevertheless, Fanning at once set about negotiating for his exchange. Fortunately, the British had not taken the few gold pieces he had brought with him on the voyage. A guard, for half a guinea, agreed to carry a message to a British friend of Americans in Gosport, who would forward the note to France. There the letter would be delivered to Doctor Franklin, chief of the three American high commissioners in Paris. If anyone could arrange for his exchange, Franklin could. The guards, it soon became evident, considered delivering messages a much easier way to make money on the side than to chase prisoners outside the prison. Besides, many of the guards, like many other Englishmen all during the Revolutionary War, were sympathetic to the American cause. Fanning spent a good part of his time while in Forton Prison learning French from French prisoners, who were billeted with the crew of the *Angelica.*

The months dragged on and there was no word from Paris and no indication that Fanning would be exchanged. Then at last he and 119 other Americans and Frenchmen were told to pack up their few belongings and prepare to sail for France with the next tide. To the tune of "Yankee Doodle," the popular rebel war tune, played by the garrison band

somewhat in derision of the American prisoners, the group
was marched down to dockside in Gosport, boarded a small
ship, and sailed for France and freedom.

The small vessel was crowded, but the men didn't mind.
They laughed and joked and sang, for some of them had
been in the naval prison for longer than Fanning. The vessel, after an uneventful voyage, dropped anchor in the harbor of Nantes, France, on the peninsula of Brittany. A great
throng of excited Bretons met them at wharfside shouting,
"*Bon! Bon! Bon!* Here come the Bostonians, who beat the
English with their great guns." For the French at that time
thought and spoke of all Americans as Bostonians.

The freed American prisoners were escorted to a big hall
where a hearty dinner had been prepared for them.

Fanning, like the other Americans, had arrived penniless
in Nantes and dressed in ragged clothing, much patched and
washed clean, but most disreputable looking for all that. So
great was the desire of the French residents to help, however,
that within days a huge purse of gold had been made up and
generous sums were distributed to the much-admired Bostonians.

After more than a year in the English naval prison Fanning now was torn between two desires—to get home to
Stonington as soon as he could, even though, with such limited funds, he probably would have to work his passage
home, or to obtain a junior officer's berth under Commodore
John Paul Jones.

For only a few days before the exchange of prisoners the prison grapevine had brought word that the famous sea rover, now a commodore in the American Navy, was fitting out a small American squadron in France. Franklin, it was said, had obtained from the French government an old battleship that Jones had renamed the *Bon Homme Richard*, or *Good Man Richard*, in honor of Benjamin Franklin, whose "Poor Richard" writings were widely acclaimed.

The *Richard* would be the flagship of the little squadron. Lorient, where the squadron was fitting out, was not too long a journey from Nantes. It had a most convenient harbor for such a venture, being an excellent port for ships of the line and other vessels, despite difficult navigation between rocks at its entrance. Well protected against storms, it also was strongly guarded by the powerful citadel of Fort Louis. Ships entering or leaving must pass within musket shot of its frowning battlements and heavy cannon.

Serving a hitch in the American Navy, small though it was, seemed to Fanning to be the more attractive plan. So, with high hopes, bolstered by the fact that he now wore clean clothes and had money in his pockets, thanks to the friendly burghers of Nantes, he set out overland for Lorient. Upon arriving, he at once laid plans to arrange a meeting with Jones.

Commodore Jones proved to be a hard man to meet, and it was widely said on the waterfront of Lorient that he already had a full crew for each of his ships. There also was the fact

that more than 100 other American seamen who had arrived
with Fanning from Forton Prison also were looking for jobs
or a chance to work their passage home to America. He
didn't have much time to waste.

So, two days after reaching Lorient, Fanning wrote a short
note to the Commodore, setting out his experience as a
Stonington sailor and privateersman. The note was written
in Fanning's excellent penmanship, his "fine copper hand,"
as many persons have described his handwriting. Even the
smallest lettering of his penmanship was as easily deciphera-
ble as printed type. He managed to borrow some red sealing
wax and used his own ring to stamp it, then persuaded an
obliging guard on the stone pier where the *Bon Homme
Richard* was moored to carry the missive to the Commodore.

Would the Commodore read a note from an unknown
person whose handwriting he did not recognize? And, even if
he did read it, would he consent to talk with an unknown
American seaman, beached in a port 3000 miles from home?

Chapter Six
MIDSHIPMAN FANNING

Fanning's thought on seeing John Paul Jones for the first time was that he was a "little runt."

Jones, indeed, stood only something over five feet, five inches. He had sandy, reddish hair, and was not at all good-looking. But there was something about the way he walked, something about the quick, nervous energy he displayed in talking, and in the motions of his hands, that conveyed a sense of dynamic enthusiasm. Fanning liked the man at once, but at the same time he felt somewhat repelled by Jones's cocksure manner. He wondered what shipping out with Jones would be like, but from the first he had almost no misgivings.

Fanning towered head and shoulders above Jones, although he was not a particularly big person, and he carried himself with as much self-assurance as the little Scotsman. Jones, as Fanning had heard in Nantes, dressed nattily in his uniform coat of blue, white waistcoat, and white breeches. Fanning, therefore, had taken care, within his limited financial means, to outfit himself in a new blue coat and breeches, with a white vest, wearing ruffles at the neck and cuffs. With a new black tricorne hat and black shoes and white stockings, he considered himself almost as well dressed as Jones. He felt quite at ease and sure of himself.

Jones was busy at the quayside when the note was handed to him. He slit the wax seal and read the contents, then turned and deliberately looked Fanning over in the most impersonal way. After which he resumed his conversation with one of his officers about some business of loading the *Richard*, completely and, Fanning thought, rather rudely ignoring his visitor.

Momentarily Fanning was surprised at the sight of the blue-and-white uniform worn by the American officers and by Jones himself. Then he grinned in quick understanding. The American naval uniform for officers at that time consisted of a blue coat, red waistcoat, and blue breeches. But Jones had insisted from the first that his officers wear a blue coat, white waistcoat, and white breeches, the more easily to deceive the Royal Navy when his ship approached an enemy vessel upon the high seas. The British then saw what appeared to be their own naval uniform on Jones's quarterdeck. When they got close enough, without their suspicions being aroused, the British ensign quickly was hauled down on Jones's ship and the American colors were run up. By that time the Commodore was near enough so that, with only a smart bit of maneuvering, he could close with and board the enemy. This form of attack was his favorite.

Jones's tight discipline was well-known—as tough as that of a ship of the Royal Navy. Such discipline helped to win sea fights, but it also explained why Jones wasn't as popular at sea as some more easy-going, however valiant, officers of the fledgling American Navy.

After what seemed an eternity of waiting, during which he felt alternately hot and cold with excitement, Fanning was almost curtly bidden to come forward to talk with the cocky Jones. The fact that Nathaniel Fanning was a native of Stonington, Connecticut, with its long tradition of seafaring, and that he had sailed in privateering expeditions evidently had impressed the Commodore. But, more important, Fanning's "fine copper hand," revealed in his note, had decided Jones. Perhaps, too, the Commodore was impressed, as others had been, by this self-possessed young man of better than medium height, a good-proportioned compact body, reddish hair and gray-blue eyes that seemed to bore into one, a strong nose and a mouth that smiled easily but could as quickly set in a firm, straight line. Even a year in Forton Prison had but slightly erased the sun-and-wind tan of his fair complexion. Perhaps, too, Jones and Fanning took an instant liking to each other, despite the Commodore's blunt warning during their brief talk that he had "kicked secretaries down the companionway in my time" and might do it again if Fanning ever displeased him.

Anyway, Jones said, although he had a full complement for the *Bon Homme Richard*, he would sign on Fanning as a midshipman. He intended, he said, soon to sail for America, but first proposed to make a six weeks' cruise around the British Isles in search of the prizes to be found in the enemy's home waters.

There was Fanning's chance both to realize his wish to sail again against the enemy with Jones and to earn his passage home. The opportunity was even better than he had dared to hope for when he set out for Lorient. He accepted the offer at once.

What if the cocky Jones did affect two gold epaulets on his narrow shoulders, instead of the one that American naval regulations provided for? What if he did have the reputation of being somewhat of a dandy? Jones might be vain, and some said he was a braggart, but his naval achievements were such that perhaps he had the right to boast of them. What if some of his men complained that he was stingy and that some officers and crew who had sailed with him had difficulty in collecting their share of prize money? None disputed Jones's reputation for fairness in all other respects. Even if he sometimes abused a lieutenant or a midshipman, he was quick to seek their apology by inviting them to share his lonely meal in the great cabin aft.

Jones's skilled, daring seamanship was legendary; his exploits aship and ashore had caused a heavy price to be put upon his head, dead or alive, by the British Admiralty. Fanning always had wanted to sail with this kind of man from the time he first went to sea. Jones might have a mean temper, as the Commodore himself admitted, but that could be overlooked for the sake of sailing with such an imaginative and daring commander. Jones was a man after Fanning's own heart; he felt he could learn much from the little Scotsman.

At Jones's direction Fanning quickly stowed his gear in a hammock next to the Commodore's great cabin aft, and then went topside alone to inspect the *Richard*. She had appeared to be a fair ship at quayside, although obviously she was quite old. The *Richard* had been an Indiaman in the merchant trade to the Far East in her younger days. Then the French government, badly in need of fighting ships, had converted her into a battleship. Now she was cut down to a razee, with her upper deck removed, making her smaller. On her lower gun deck Fanning found she carried six eighteen-pounders. On her gun deck she mounted twenty-eight twelve- and nine-pounders. She carried six six-pounders on her quarterdeck and spar deck, a total of forty guns. She would have a crew of 380—officers, men, and boys. The armament was not much, considering she might have to fight some of England's most modern ships of the line. Nor was it a very heavy complement of men, since Jones was almost certain to lose some by desertion and in battle. And, if the Commodore had any luck in capturing prizes, he would have to detail many men for crews to take the seized vessels into a French port.

Fanning tested the deck planking with the point of his sea knife and found that it was beginning to rot. The *Richard* had new masts and spars as well as new armament, rigging, and canvas, but he wondered how maneuverable she was or how well she could fight. With a lesser sailor than Jones few men would have cared to ship out on her.

The *Richard* would sail as the flagship of a small squadron that was to include the *Alliance*, a thirty-six-gun frigate, under the command of Captain Pierre Landais, a Frenchman; the *Pallas*, thirty-two guns, Captain Denis Nicholas Cottineau; the *Cerf*, eighteen guns, Captain Joseph Varage; the *Vengeance*, twelve guns, Captain Phillipe Nicolas-Ricot. Fanning could believe the stories he had heard in Lorient—that Jones had been obliged to recruit raw peasants from off the farms of Brittany for part of the *Richard's* crew. The truth of the rumor was only too evident from the awkward way some of these men went about their work aboard ship. Others of the crew, in addition to Americans and Frenchmen, included English naval prisoners who had volunteered for duty in the American service. About two thirds of the men were Americans, but Fanning thought most of them were a dirty lot. He reassured himself that if any man could mold this nondescript crew into a fighting unit, Jones could.

It would not be quite as easy as that, Fanning decided one afternoon when Captain Landais came aboard the *Richard* for a conference with Jones. The Frenchman appeared to be not only coolly arrogant, but somewhat irrational. As secretary to the Commodore, Midshipman Fanning was present during most of the conference in Jones's cabin. Apparently Landais was angry because Jones and not he had been chosen to command the expedition. Landais was a former officer in the French Navy, but his hot temper and irrational habits had caused him to be eased out of the service. He had joined the young American Navy and already had earned the reputation of being a man with whom it was hard to get along. Fanning felt sure that Jones would have trouble with Landais before the cruise ended.

Had it not been for powerful influences in Paris, Jones certainly would not have given Landais command of the *Alliance.* Probably he would not have had the man in the squadron in any capacity. The *Alliance* was such a trim little frigate that she deserved a better captain than Landais. Under the right skipper she could have given a good account of herself in any fight. But already, on the way over from America under the command of Landais, there had been near mutiny on several occasions and her officers and men were on poor terms, with consequently weak discipline. She

was anything but a happy ship. Fanning didn't like the prospect. In a tight jam at sea, the *Richard* would need the support of every gun in the little squadron and the loyal cooper-
ation of every officer and man. But would she get that kind
of help from Captain Landais?

Fanning wondered how Jones, a most impatient man, had
the patience to put up with the intrigue of the French court
in Versailles, and particularly that which centered around
naval help for the United States. There had been delays of
many kinds in fitting out the little squadron and most of
them for such trivial reasons that mere inefficiency in the
French Ministry of Marine could not have been the only
reason. Much of the intrigue, Jones's correspondence showed,
centered around Captain Landais. Two of the American high
commissioners in Paris still were insisting, even on the eve of
the sailing of the squadron, that Landais should command the
expedition. Only the stubborn will and the diplomatic skill of
Benjamin Franklin had kept Jones in command, with the rank
of commodore.

Finally Jones decided there had to be a showdown at the
top, and one day he summarily ordered Fanning to accompany him on a hurried trip to Paris. He would need, he said,
a competent secretary to be present at his talks with Doctor
Franklin; Charles Gravier, the Count de Vergennes, the
king's favorite and foreign minister, who was friendly toward
the American cause and a confirmed enemy of England; the
French Ministry of Marine; and others who could be of help.

The Commodore was very popular at the French court in Versailles, near Paris, as the result of his daring voyages against the English. There would be compensation for the hard work and long hours ashore, the Commodore assured his midshipman-secretary. Usually closed doors would be opened to his assistant. Besides, there would be the opportunity of meeting the great Doctor Franklin, whom all France adored for his simplicity, wisdom, kindness and for his scholastic, literary, and scientific achievements. Not too many persons, even those close to King Louis XVI, realized then what great influence Franklin exerted with his skill in diplomacy. And he was almost as successful in manipulating British statesmen as Frenchmen without their knowing it.

Jones took passage for himself and Midshipman Fanning on public stagecoach, an expensive but fast mode of travel from Lorient to Paris. Pulled by six horses, which were changed every ten or twelve miles, the coach jounced over the unpaved dirt road at an average speed of ten to twelve miles an hour. The trip wasn't comfortable, but one could "make good time," for those days, and when one became tired from the ride there always was a place to stop off for a brief rest and an appetizing meal.

Soon Fanning realized that every few miles the coach passed a pair of well-mounted young men dressed in blue uniform coats with red facings and cuffs, red waistcoat, and pantaloons. Upon the left sleeve just above the cuff they wore an inch-wide gold lace band. Each man was armed with a brace of long-barrelled pistols, a broadsword carried in a black-leather scabbard, and a light horseman's musket slung over the shoulders. Sometimes there were four of these men riding together, and now and then he counted six of the roving mounted policemen in a group.

Jones, who had ridden over the road to Paris many times, explained that these young men, usually the sons of noblemen, were a part of the far-flung French police system that ranged the country from one end to the other. They were an auxiliary police force, paid directly by the king, and their special job was to prevent highway robbery, burglary, and other serious crimes, to protect otherwise unguarded villages, to arrest deserters from the armed forces, and to round up escaped criminals. Jones assured his young midshipman-secretary that highway robbers and burglars were almost unknown at that time in France, so well did these men do their job.

Doctor Franklin's beautiful villa in Passy, outside Paris and near the French king's palace at Versailles, was the center of much diplomatic and social activity. But Franklin always had time for a friendly and usually helpful visit with young men from his own country. "My children," he called these visitors. He was particularly interested in naval men, for their services were vital to the American cause, and he had helped to set up several daring privateersmen, who preyed upon English commerce. Franklin sensed more than any other American patriot leader, save Washington, the need to carry the war to the enemy upon the sea, especially in the waters of the British Isles, where it would really hurt.

So it was natural that when Franklin learned from Commodore Jones of Nathaniel Fanning's seafaring background and of his three cruises as a privateersman—one as a prizemaster—that he would make himself agreeable. Fanning's own personality helped, too. From that time he knew that, whatever his adventures in France might be, he could count on Franklin's friendship and help. For Fanning now was determined, one way or another, to obtain the command of his own privateer.

Thanks to both Franklin and Jones, social doors were opened to Midshipman Fanning, as Jones had promised. Soon Fanning became popular in his own right, sharing some of the social appeal of Jones himself. In this environment his French improved so quickly that soon he learned to speak the language fluently. He attended gay parties at Passy and at Versailles, where his graceful dancing made him a desirable partner. The visit was all too brief to suit Fanning, for a whole new world had been opened to him. But, however pleasant the experience, he was a young man with a single, all-consuming objective, and he tried to make his social contacts serve as a help in furthering his ambition. He was laying the foundation for the future, well knowing that he had no chance at the moment to aspire to a rank higher than midshipman and secretary to Commodore Jones.

Once Jones had assured himself that he had Doctor
Franklin's absolute backing, which carried with it the whole
power of the French Ministry of Marine and of King Louis
XVI himself, the Commodore hastened back at once to
Lorient by fast coach, Nathaniel Fanning with him. Now,
although Jones must stifle his intense dislike of the insubor-
dinate Landais, he at least had the authority to compel the
French captain to obey orders. Or so the Commodore thought.

Chapter Seven
CAPTAIN OF THE MAIN TOP

At last, on August 14, 1779, Jones sailed from Lorient in command of the little squadron.

Two days later the *Richard* took as a prize an English ship laden with bales of silk. Cruising around the Orkney Islands in the North Sea, Jones captured or destroyed sixteen vessels and burned four laden with coal. There were other captures, but these incidents were minor. Jones chafed. He was after bigger game.

Not until September 22 did his luck change. The *Bon Homme Richard* was close off Flamborough Head, which is a little more than halfway from London to Edinburgh, Scotland, when Jones was informed by a spy that a convoy of forty unarmed merchant ships was headed for Leith Harbor, Edinburgh. Only two fighting ships protected the convoy.

Jones sent Midshipman Fanning aloft with a spyglass to look for the convoy, then ordered his consort vessels to set a course for Flamborough Head. The little cutter *Cerf* already had returned to France, so Jones, with only four fighting ships, might be taking on a strong British fleet, despite the report that there were only two warships. But the risk was worthwhile. This chance was his big one.

Fanning quickly gained his lookout post aloft, slid open the sections of the telescope, and carefully swept the horizon. He was calm and deliberate, despite his excitement. His job required calm nerves and an accurate report. The safety of Jones's little squadron might depend upon him.

Off to starboard he could see the white chalk cliffs of Flamborough Head. He could make out the fishing village that crowned this jutting point of England, which stuck out into the North Sea. Fanning squinted into the sunlight. It silvered the water so that it shone with the brilliance of diamonds. Suddenly his slow sweep of the telescope stopped. He focused a little to starboard of the *Richard's* course. There was the convoy!

"Ahoy the deck!" he called. "I make out twenty-five sail of ships, sir! And more coming up fast!"

The voice of the Commodore came back, and Fanning could see the blue-coated figure in black cocked hat, striding

Foula I.
Shetland Is.
Fair I.
N. Ronaldsay
Orkney Is.
Flannan Is.
NORTH
HEBRIDES
MINCH
St. Kilda
ATLANTIC
SCOTLAND
OCEAN
DUNDEE
NORTH
Firth of Forth
SEA
LEITH
GLASGOW EDINBURGH
LONDONDERRY
NEWCASTLE
BELFAST
SCARBOROUGH
Flamborough Hd.
I. of Man
JONES' COURSE TO
HULL
THE TEXEL AFTER
R. Humber
BATTLE
IRELAND
IRISH
Anglesey
Slyne
SEA
Head
DUBLIN
WALES
ENGLAND
Skelligs
THE
DOWNS
CORK DUNGARVAN
LONDON
GOODWIN
Thames R.
SANDS DUNKIRK
DOVER
I. of Wight
RYE
CALAIS
PORTSMOUTH
Strait of Dover
Land's End CORNWALL
DIEPPE
English Channel
LE HAVRE
CHERBOURG
ATLANTIC
Channel Is.
FRANCE
OCEAN
Ushant
MORLAIX
BREST
0 35 70 105 140
LORIENT
Cruise of
NAUTICAL MILES
Ile de Groix
BON HOMME
Belle I.
RICHARD
AUGUST–SEPTEMBER,
ROUTE ....
1779

the quarterdeck. "Can you make out the strength of the enemy?"

Fanning put the spyglass to his eye again, pointing it this time more toward the headland. And there they were! Two armed ships! One he made out to be a British frigate of the latest class. The other ship was a big, armed merchantman. These vessels were protecting the convoy. Now, as his eyes began to focus better, he saw the two warships change course. They were moving out from Flamborough Head, in line of battle. They had sighted the *Bon Homme Richard* and were going into action.

"Ahoy the deck! Two ships, sir—a king's frigate of fifty guns and an armed merchant ship of twenty-two guns," Fanning reported.

"Very good, Mr. Fanning. Keep your station until relieved. And let me know the minute you have more to report." Then Fanning heard Jones bawl, "Mr. Dale! Call the crew to quarters! Clear for action!"

There came a faint "Aye, aye, sir," and Lieutenant Richard Dale repeated the Commodore's orders. Fanning did not need to glance below to see men scurrying to remove every piece of movable equipment, to tighten down unneeded hatches, to open gunport lids on the cannon. He knew, too, that the "powder monkeys" already were scrambling below to the magazine to start bringing up powder and cannon balls topside. This work principally belonged to the young boys who had signed on as members of the *Richard's* crew.

Then again, in Jones's voice, "Signal the *Alliance* and the *Pallas* to close in and support us."

Fanning hoped desperately that Captain Landais in the *Alliance* would obey the order. Her guns would put the *Richard* on almost equal terms with the two enemy ships. But as the *Richard's* signals fluttered aloft, he sensed that Landais would not help the man he so greatly hated.

Topsail after topsail popped over the hazy line that divided sky and water. Fanning did not report each new sail, but gave his attention mostly to the maneuvering of the two British warships. Already the merchant vessels, having sighted the little American squadron, and acting upon signal from their consorts, were crowding on all sail and scurrying for the safety of shoal waters. He wished that the *Vengeance*, which was chasing a sail to the northeast, could return in time for the now certain battle, but this assistance was too much to expect.

Captain Cottineau of the *Pallas* had changed course in answer to signals from the *Richard*. She had been chasing the armed merchant ship, later identified as the *Countess of Scarborough,* twenty-two guns. Now, coldly calculating as he watched, Fanning saw the king's frigate swing her yards and head more directly for the *Richard*. Jones, since he could not count on the loyalty of Landais in the *Alliance*, and with his other ships away on other missions, would have to fight alone.

Below, Fanning could see and hear the swift preparations for battle. Cannon were being run in and swabbed out with water, loaded with bags of powder and with cartridges, balls, and wadding. Then they were run out again, their black snouts sticking through the gunports. Gun crews were stripped down to the waist. Decks were sanded, for the wooden planking soon was certain to be slippery with blood; water buckets were filled with sea water and placed in handy spots, for there was almost sure to be fire, and it might break out in many parts of the ship at once when the action got under way. Boarding nettings were being triced up along the bulwarks, the better to defend the ship if she closed with the enemy.

Now Fanning could smell the acrid smoke from smoldering slow matches as they were passed out to the captains of gun crews. These bits of burning rope, especially treated and attached to long, forked metal rods, called linstocks, were used to spark powder in the touchholes at the top rear of a cannon. This ignition fired the powder charge. A gun captain could increase or decrease the range of his weapon by the amount of powder he used in the gun. He could elevate the cannon or lower the muzzle by means of crowbars on a series of gun-carriage steps.

Occasionally, as he glanced below, Fanning could see a grimy-faced "powder monkey," as the young boys were called, passing up, chain fashion, pound sacks of powder and heavy cannon balls. In this manner ammunition was sent up to the gun decks from the magazine, deep in the ship's hold.

The work was hard, dirty, and thankless, but he knew the boys loved the excitement of it.

He heard Jones give the order to "take in all courses, clew up topgallants." Topmen swarmed up the ratlines and inched out along the safety lines that hung below the yards, to take in all but topsails and jibs. This slim battle canvas would make the ship more maneuverable and help it to jockey for a favorable battle position. Seldom did a vessel go into action with all sail set, although this rule was not invariable. Up to that minute, Jones had kept set his principal sails, which gave the *Richard* more speed, in order to take advantage of the light wind and to close sooner with the enemy. Now that he was nearer to the enemy he was hauling these bigger sails up, where they would be out of the way. In the event that a spar or mast should be shot away, the sails, thus clewed up, would become less of a hazard for the ship. Much would depend upon Jones's seamanship as well as the accurate fire of the gun crews.

The British frigate was painted yellow; the *Richard* was solid black—hull, masts, and spars. Then Fanning recognized the Britisher. He had heard of her back in Lorient. She was the *Serapis*, very fast and well armed with the newest design in cannon, commanded by Captain Richard Pearson, one of the bravest and most able of King George's naval officers. Pitted against even John Paul Jones, Pearson would be a dangerous foe. Neither man, it was said, knew the meaning of physical fear.

Fanning trained his glass again upon the shore, above the bald, white cliffs of Flamborough Head. In the late afternoon sunlight he could see black dots moving about, and he knew they were men and women gathering to watch the coming battle. He felt a little sickened when he remembered that, despite her new rigging and her new sails, the *Richard* really was little better than a fourteen-year-old tub. With her rotten timbers and sprung boom, she was unfit to fight a king's ship, especially a new one that outgunned and surely would outsail her. What chance did the *Richard* have against the *Serapis*?

The *Richard* was a sluggish vessel—not a "cranky" ship, one that is hard to handle—but ungainly. She never had been a lively ship. She could be expected now to do her best, but would that be good enough, even in the expert hands of John Paul Jones? She was coming up against the best in the king's Navy. With her new armament the *Richard* was a fair equal to a thirty-six-gun frigate. But in sailing qualities she still was like the lumbering old East Indiaman that for so many years she had been.

Fanning's confidence returned somewhat as he heard the calm but insistent voice of the Commodore hailing him from the quarterdeck. "Mr. Fanning! How many sail do you make out now?"

"Forty-one, sir." He couldn't be sure, but that was the figure Jones later would report to the king of France. Fan-

ning always would believe that he might have missed one
ship, and that there were forty-two sail in the convoy.

"Mr. Fanning, report to the deck!"

Fanning folded the Commodore's telescope, held it tightly
under one arm, swung over the side of the maintop platform,
took the ratlines two at a time in his descent, and quickly
stood before Jones on the quarterdeck. The Commodore was
an awe-inspiring figure, despite his small stature. Men respected him, but they greatly feared him, too, not only as
master of the ship and the sole custodian of their lives, but as
a man.

Jones, in the hours Fanning had been aloft, had changed
into a new blue uniform coat, with white vest and breeches,
a new black cocked hat, white hose, and black, silver-buckled
shoes. Even when going into battle he still was somewhat of a
dandy, always carefully dressed. Not a hair of Jones's almost
red hair was out of place, so far as Fanning could see, when
the Commodore removed his hat briefly to wipe his brow.
The hair shone like burnished gold in the bright afternoon
sunlight. His bronzed cheeks were flushed with the sup-
pressed excitement of the chase and his exertions in getting
the ship ready for action. His thin-lipped mouth was tight,
but not unkind.

"Have you eaten, Mr. Fanning?"

"No, sir." Only then, indeed, did Fanning realize that he
was hungry. He had not eaten since early morning.

"Get below and feed the inner man," said the Commodore. "Then report to me."

"Aye, aye, sir."

When, a little later, Fanning returned to the quarterdeck, the Commodore was giving orders to two younger midshipmen. Jones turned to him. "Mr. Fanning, you will command maintop. I am giving you fifteen marines and four sailors. The foretop will be manned by ten marines and four sailors. The mizzen by six marines and two sailors, both under top captains."

"Aye, aye, sir."

"Until the enemy's tops are cleared," added Jones, "you will direct your fire into their tops, using muskets, blunderbusses, cowhorns, and swivels. We must silence their tops before we can close and board."

"Aye, aye, sir." Fanning saluted, then sprinted for the larboard shrouds, climbed the ratlines to the maintop, and took stock of his supplies of arms and ammunition. He stood on the wooden platform at the top of the great mast that carried the mainsail. The platform was protected by a circular rope railing, but the footing was none too secure when the ship rolled or pitched. Hence, aiming a musket or a swivel gun onto the deck or into the tops of an enemy ship required steadiness of hand and nerve, and a good balance on well-braced feet.

Soon the marines and sailors assigned to him were handing up weapons and ammunition. These supplies he lashed securely to the rope railing, so they would not fall into the sea or onto the deck below. All were to be covered, too, so that sparks or gunfire from the enemy tops would not set off the ammunition.

Swivels and blunderbusses were mounted and secured, either to larboard or to starboard of the maintop. The quarters would be close for twenty men on such a small platform, so each man was assigned to a station. The maintop might have to be crossed at any time, too, by men who were sent aloft to handle topsails or the mainsail. Similar activity was to be seen from the foretop and mizzen top.

Fanning looked over the deepening gray of the sea when preparations for battle had been completed. Night was coming on, but the ships, because of contrary winds, were yet some distance apart. The *Serapis* was a handsome vessel. As she veered somewhat and he could see her broadside guns, she showed a double row of "teeth"—two rows of gunports with the black muzzles of her cannon sticking out. Fanning thought, even at that distance, he could see the smudge of her slow matches along the upper bulwark. Her gunners would be standing by for the order to fire. Again he smelled the acrid fumes of the *Richard's* slow matches. He wished he were below, for he liked to help work the guns. But his job as captain of the maintop was more important now than handling a gun on deck. From their tops a deadly small-arms fire could be poured into the enemy's tops and later, if he were lucky, onto her decks. He sweated, striving to calm his growing impatience. It was hard, waiting for the action to begin.

Bits of bunting inched to the peak as the signal halyards creaked in their blocks. Fanning just could make out the message. The Commodore was signaling for the *Pallas* to continue her chase of the *Countess of Scarborough*. The twenty-two-gun consort of the *Serapis* was doing her best to escape, but Fanning guessed she would lose the race. Captain Cottineau of the *Pallas* almost certainly would have her within the hour.

The signal halyards creaked again. This time the Commodore had signalled an order for Landais in the *Alliance* to close in support of the *Richard*. Between them they should be able to finish off the *Serapis* with a heavy cross fire. But Fanning turned away in disgust and anger as Landais deliberately stood off. Landais, it now appeared certain, would not help Jones, even in the face of the enemy! Whether the action was the result of cowardice or hatred didn't much matter. It was not only rank insubordination, it was treason. The *Richard* must fight the battle alone against greatly superior odds.

Fanning could guess that Jones's bronzed face was white with anger, but there was nothing the Commodore could do for the moment to compel his subordinate to obey orders. For now the *Serapis* was almost within cannon shot. The next few minutes might decide the outcome of the battle. The *Alliance*, in the near distance, was tacking and filling as though Landais merely were watching the scene. The *Pallas*, having taken the *Countess of Scarborough* and put a prize crew aboard

her, came foaming up, but she, too, stood off, instead of coming
to grips with the British frigate.

A ship's bell sounded. Eight smart strokes of the hammer.
It was eight bells! The *Richard* had taken all of this time,
since about noon, to come close enough to the enemy to
engage him, so light had been the wind.

There came a hail across the darkening water. "What ship
is that?" The Britisher was asking the question. Fanning just
could make out the tall, dark form of the officer on the frigate's quarterdeck, speaking trumpet in hand.

The reply came promptly from Jones himself. "Come a
little closer and I'll tell you!"

The ships now were within cannon range and Jones's in-
solent answer brought from the *Serapis* a whole broadside,
fired from her upper tier of guns. There came the crackling
fire of pistols as British marines in the frigate's tops replied to
the fire of Fanning's own topmen. Smoke and flame belched
almost continually from his own and the maintop of the
enemy.

Upon the echo of the broadside from the *Serapis* there
came the crash of the *Richard's* own battery of eighteen-
pounders. A sheet of flame shot from an open hatchway forward, and even above the hideous din aloft Fanning could
hear the screams of badly burned and wounded men. Three
of the *Richard's* eighteen-pounders had exploded. Dr. Law-
rence Brook, the ship's surgeon, would have more wounded
men than he could treat.

Jones ordered his eighteen-pounders abandoned rather than risk the lives of more of his men by firing them. The remaining gun crews were ordered topside to help on the upper gun deck. But the first enemy broadside had put out of action most of the nine twelve-pounders. Cannon were strewn about the deck at crazy angles, wooden gun carriages were askew or blown to bits, gunners were down, torn by great splinters from the gun carriages and the deck planking. The only effective cannon that Jones had left and that he could bring to bear were those on the quarterdeck.

Fanning felt a hand tugging at his left elbow and turned to find a powder-smoked sailor trying to get his attention.

"The Commodore's compliments, sir, and he says he's depending on his topmen to save the day. Most of our cannon are already out of action." The man gave Fanning a quick report of the results of that first terrible enemy broadside.

So hard had the *Richard* shivered under the pounding that Fanning scarcely had to be told what had happened. He knew also that she must have received more than one eighteen-pound enemy shot "twixt wind and water." With a hole in her hull below the waterline she would ship water fast. Men who were badly needed to work the vessel and her remaining guns would have to man the pumps to keep her afloat.

Topmen were out on the spar now. Fanning heard the creak of tackle below as Jones brought, or wore, the ship around. He was trying to tack into a good battle position.

True, with most of his guns out of action, he could do little by way of a broadside against the fifty-gun enemy ship. But he could try. The situation was all but hopeless—the *Richard* was nearly beaten, except that she was under command of John Paul Jones. Fanning took heart at the thought and tried to make every shot count from his musket.

The *Serapis* handled more easily than the *Richard*, as Fanning had feared. The first broadside seemed to have either damaged or shot away the older ship's rudder.

The wind still held light and already Captain Pearson of the *Serapis* had found that he could outsail the *Richard*, despite Jones's great skill as a seaman. The British frigate wore ship, coming about. Slowly, because of the wind, she came in under the stern of the *Richard*, raking her fore and aft. Even if all the *Richard's* guns had been working she would have had to take this terrible punishment, since the other ship so easily outmaneuvered her. Always, Fanning had been taught, since his first days aboard a warship, the effort should be made to catch the enemy bow-on or stern-to and fire a broadside that would sweep the length of her deck. That tactic was what the *Serapis* was doing now.

Terrible carnage had been effected on the decks of the *Richard*. Because of the darkness and the thick, almost suffocating smoke, he sensed rather than saw what was happening below. Men were dead, dying, or wounded. Great splinters of wood, torn from the decks or from masts and spars and wooden gun mounts, were as deadly weapons as cannon shot and musket ball, hand pike or cutlass. And, more often than not, the wounds they made were more difficult to treat.

There followed a long interval in which he lost all sense of time. Jones, despite his lack of a rudder, skillfully was trying to maneuver the ship by her topsails and jibs into such a position as would bar Captain Pearson from raking her again. Now and then, through the din of musket and pistol fire, mostly from the ships' tops, Fanning could hear the calm voice of the Commodore, ordering, encouraging, stirring his men to even greater effort. Fanning felt a quick warmth of comradeship with this leader for whom men gave their best and surpassed it with even greater effort.

Then the *Serapis* attempted another maneuver. She inched toward the forefoot, where stem meets keel at the bow, of the *Richard*. The *Richard* rocked and shook as another British broadside raked her fore and aft. More men went down. With agonizing repetition the British frigate continued to pierce the hull of the American ship with solid shot from successive broadsides.

"Lay her aboard! Lay her aboard!" Jones kept shouting to his officers. Indeed, Fanning thought, that would be the only salvation for the *Richard*. If Jones could bring her abreast of the *Serapis*, lash the two ships together, and board the Britisher, they might have a chance to win the battle. He had little doubt of the result if the men of the *Richard* gained the deck of the *Serapis*. The Americans were at their best when fighting on an enemy ship's deck, hand-to-hand.

There was a momentary lull in the din. Then Jones's voice came again, loud and clear, "Lay her aboard!"

Fanning's pulses leaped. If Jones's maneuver succeeded the Commodore would be depending even more upon his topmen. Marskmen might direct such a deadly fire onto the Britisher's top decks as to drive her officers and crew below, giving the boarding party an excellent chance to capture the enemy ship. For evidently, even with his guns silenced, his hull shot through and through, so that the *Richard* was in a sinking condition, the Commodore was determined to capture the frigate. One thing seemed certain—the *Richard* could take little more of such terrible punishment.

Fanning saw the *Serapis* again moving slowly toward the *Richard's* forefoot. There came the grinding crash of splintering wood. What Jones had been unable to do with his disabled ship, the light wind of the night had done for him— it had crashed the *Serapis* right into the *Richard*! The American ship's jibboom had fouled the Britisher's starboard mizzen shrouds.

"That's well, my lads! We've got her now!" Jones cried in a loud, clear, exultant voice.

The enemy, discovering that their ship was afoul of the *Richard,* tried desperately to get clear. Theirs was the advantage if they could stand off and continue to hull and perhaps dismast the American. The British warship let go an anchor, trying to get clear by the natural action of wind and wave in separating the two vessels.

Then there occurred one of those unexpected freaks of nature that serve sometimes indirectly to decide an issue. The wind, which had been light all evening, suddenly died to an almost dead calm. The British maneuver of dropping an anchor had failed. The Americans watched with cheers as the *Serapis* swung around upon the *Richard*. There was another rending crash and the jibboom of the *Serapis* crashed into the sea. Her jibstay dangled over the *Richard's* poop.

In a momentary lifting of the thick smoke Fanning saw Jones and John Burband, the sailing master, spring forward, seize the enemy's dangling jibstay, and quickly secure it to the mizzenmast of the *Richard*. The two ships now lay stern to bow, the *Richard* secured stern-to to the bow of the *Serapis* by means of the jibstay tied to her mizzenmast. Both ships rode to the anchor the Britisher had put over. Jones's quick action in securing the broken jibstay, in effect, had lashed the two ships as securely as though he had run alongside the enemy with grappling irons.

The Britisher took quick advantage. Boarding parties scrambled over the *Richard's* bulwarks. Fiercely they were repulsed. The guns of the *Serapis* were as effectively silenced as those of the *Richard*. The ships were so close together that cannon could not be worked effectively. The men of both ships fired at each other with small arms through the open gunports. Rattling musketry fire swept the tops and the decks more furiously than ever.

Suddenly Fanning listened more intently. The ragged fire

from the tops of the *Serapis* had ceased. Evidently the topmen
of the *Richard* had cleared the rigging of the enemy ship. He
turned to his men, "Her tops are silenced! Fire onto her
deck! Pick off her officers!"

At last, because of the dying wind, the *Richard* had the
advantage. If her own topmen could drive the crew of the
Serapis below deck with deadly small-arms fire, a boarding
party from the American vessel, although greatly outnumbered, might have a fighting chance to capture her.

At that moment a glare appeared in the night sky. The
enemy's light sails had caught fire. Within minutes her
tarred rigging had ignited. With the two ships locked together in such a tight death embrace, the *Richard's* rigging,
too, soon would be ablaze. Already the flames from the
Serapis were leaping dangerously close to the *Richard.* If
Fanning and his men, and those of the foretop and mizzen
top were caught aloft, there would be no escape. Perhaps it
already was too late to shinny down the ratlines to the temporary safety of the deck.

But Fanning had no thought of saving himself or his men
by such an expedient. His maintop was walled in by leaping
tongues of fire, and there was no time to haul water from the
sea to put them out. The blaze must be fought now, with
what means they had aloft.

He ordered his men to strip off their uniform coats, setting
the example himself, and for the next few minutes there was
a great flailing of cloth as tongues of flame sought to reach

the maintop. Fanning used his sea jacket until it was eaten almost to the buttons by fire, then threw it away, ripped off his trousers, and used them as a fire-fighting flail. All the while he was fearful that a spark might reach a powder box or a loaded weapon on the narrow platform. It seemed hours, but was really only a few minutes, before the fire was under control. Even so there was danger that it might break out again, but for the moment the sacrifice of coat and trousers had paid off.

Then Fanning heard a sudden commotion astern. On the quarterdeck of the *Richard* he saw in the bright moonlight the ship's carpenter and the master-at-arms. "Quarters! Quarters! For God's sake, quarters! Our ship is sinking!" one of the men shouted above the din.

The two subofficers of the *Richard* were offering to surrender the ship. They were calling to the *Serapis* for quarters just as their own vessel might have a chance of victory. Where was Commodore Jones? By whose authority did these two cowards so shamelessly offer to surrender?

The bright moonlight now flooding the two ships revealed the two frantic men running like scared rabbits toward the ensign gaff, with the intention of hauling down the American colors. They evidently did not know that the ensign had been torn away when the jibboom of the *Serapis* was carried by the board.

Fanning spied Jones. The Commodore was in a towering rage. He had been forward, upon the forecastle, when the two men had come from below, shouting that the *Richard* carried four feet of water in her hold, that Jones and all the other officers had been killed, and that the ship must be given up. The Commodore had run aft as fast as he could, considering the great litter upon the deck and the great number of wounded men. He reached the poop just as the carpenter and the master-at-arms got to the shot-away ensign gaff.

"What cowardly rascals are these? Shoot 'em! Kill 'em!" shouted Jones. Then, both his pistols being empty, Jones hurled the weapons, butt forward, one after the other, at the carpenter and the master-at-arms. His aim was good, despite his rage, for Fanning saw both men go down. But so great was their fear of the Commodore that both men quickly scrambled to their feet and fled below.

The fire in other parts of the *Richard* had been controlled now as there came a hail from the *Serapis*: "If you ask for quarters," an officer inquired, "why don't you strike your flag?"

Jones seized a speaking trumpet. "Aye, aye, we'll do it when we can fight no longer! But I expect you to strike first. I've just begun to fight!"

There came a cheer from the *Richard's* tops and from the main deck at these defiant words. Then there was a sharp renewal of cannon fire. The *Serapis* had brought four of her starboard upper deck guns to bear upon the *Richard*. These cannon must be silenced at once; otherwise Jones's advantage would be lost.

Quickly Fanning appraised the situation. The ships lay so closely together that their main yards were nearly locked. There was not too great a distance from one maintop to the other. By a quick maneuver he and his men should be able to cross from one top to the other and take over the maintop of the *Serapis*. The idea was daring and, he realized, perhaps foolhardy. It meant he would be leaving his assigned post in the heat of battle, but he could serve the *Richard* better if he were on the enemy's maintop. In any event, he must take full responsibility for the action, since there was no time to get permission. Such a move meant he would be boarding the *Serapis* without authority, and for this conduct he could be court-martialed. If by some chance the two vessels became separated, he and his men would be trapped and would become prisoners. But without hesitation he turned to his men, all of whom fortunately had escaped with no more than minor burns in fighting the fire.

"Come on, lads! Her maintop is clear. Let's take it over! We'll clear her main deck with muskets and grenades and silence that battery!"

There came a ringing cheer from the battle-blackened men. Every one of their muscles ached, as did his. Some were blistered on hands and feet, as he was. Their uniforms had been discarded in fighting the blaze and they were nearly naked, as he was. Most of them had lost their head coverings, as he had. But there was in them, as there was in him, an urge to greater effort. They knew, as he did, that if the decks of the *Serapis* could be cleared of fighting men, and that lone battery of four cannon put out of action, Jones could call "Boarders away!" with every hope of victory.

Men seized muskets and pistols, unlashed swivel guns and powder kegs, threw cannon balls and hand grenades into canvas bags. Thus heavily burdened they inched gingerly across their maintop onto the *Serapis*. There were no foemen to fight. Most of the enemy had been killed or wounded and those left alive had fled below. From their new vantage point the Americans had a clear view, as much as the smoke of battle permitted, of the littered deck of the *Serapis* and the battery of belching cannon.

Then, with cool deliberation, Fanning directed an effective fire upon the enemy deck. Within minutes he saw men fleeing down her hatches to the lower gun deck. Thus they sought to save themselves from the deadly American musketry fire from their own maintop. The lone battery of four guns, however, still was in action, firing rhythmically into the men on the *Richard's* unprotected decks.

"Pick off the officers," Fanning called. The marines and sailors of the maintop crew had been especially chosen by Jones for their proven marksmanship, and already their fire had driven most of the defenders of the *Serapis's* main gun deck below. One by one the officers of the enemy's lone gun crew were picked off. A blunderbuss was brought to bear, scattering lead pellets in a thin spray across the deck. A swivel gun belched from the captured maintop, sending its small ball into the battery for a direct hit.

Fanning, musket in hand, could see an officer desperately trying to rally the remaining men of the gun crew for another salvo into the *Richard*. The officer was having a hard time. Once the men broke and ran, but they returned to their guns as the officer waved his sword and shouted. Before Fanning again could squeeze the trigger on his reloaded musket, a shot rang out. It was so close that it nearly deafened him. Silently the officer with the waving sword fell to the deck. The gun crew broke and ran for cover. They ducked and dodged behind a mast, behind the wreckage of a broken spar, then scrambled down a partly opened hatchway to the lower gun deck.

"Hand me a grenade!" Fanning rapped out the order above the din and felt the cold metal in his hand as a sailor silently handed him the weapon. Another sailor stood ready to light the fuse with a linstock that had been used to fire the swivel gun. There was a clear view of the hatch down which the last of the *Serapis's* crewmen had fled. It had been left open in their haste to reach comparative safety as the men had squeezed through a two-foot opening.

The ships were rocking gently in a light swell, and Fanning realized that this throw must allow for the roll of the ship. "Wait," he cautioned the sailor, as the man would have lighted the grenade fuse. Then, as the ship steadied between swells: "Now!"

The fuse sputtered as the slow match was applied. Fanning
leaned far over the edge of the *Serapis's* maintop platform,
took careful aim, and hurled the grenade. The weapon
found its mark, hurtled through the narrow hatch opening,
and he waited for the explosion. When it came it sounded
like the dull roar of a swivel gun below deck, but he would
not know until much later its terrible effect. Twenty of the
Serapis's men were killed and as many more wounded when
the grenade set off loose cartridges that powder monkeys had
left lying on the planking of the lower gun deck.

At any moment Fanning expected to hear "Boarders
away!" It was time for the one remaining tactic by which
Jones could hope to capture the British frigate. The order
might have come then, but at that moment there was a tremendous roar of cannon off the *Richard's* larboard beam, the
side exposed to the sea. A frigate had borne down upon the
locked ships and was firing upon the *Richard.* For an agonizing moment he thought another British warship had come
upon them. Then he recognized the lines and rigging of the
other vessel. It was the *Alliance!* Captain Landais was firing
upon his own consort, the *Richard!*

The traitor! thought Fanning, but then he wondered if in
the confusion of battle the French captain might have been
mistaken. Perhaps he thought he was firing upon the *Serapis.*
But how could he, even by moonlight, when the British ship
was painted yellow and the American black?

Within minutes the *Richard* showed her identification

lanterns placed in a horizontal line upon the fore, main, and mizzen shrouds. They were to inform the captain of the *Alliance* that he was firing upon one of his consorts. The French broadside had killed eleven of Jones's men and wounded several others.

Fanning continued to wait for the order for "Boarders away!" Even from the *Serapis's* maintop he could see men lining the bulwark of the *Richard*, cutlass, pistol, or boarding pike in hand. There still was no life to be seen aboard the *Serapis*. Her remaining officers and men were below, taking what cover they could from the deadly fire from their own maintop.

Again the *Alliance* worked past the offside of the *Richard* and fired another broadside into her. There was no doubt now that Landais deliberately was trying to sink his old enemy, Commodore Jones. Doubtless he intended afterward to capture the already badly crippled *Serapis* and take all the glory himself.

That this betrayal should have happened just at the moment when victory seemed certain made Landais' action all the more scoundrelly. But the French captain had not yet finished his evil design. He swung around under the *Richard's* stern and fired another broadside, raking her fore and aft. Fanning, still firing at every occasional head that appeared on the gun deck of the *Serapis,* managed to keep a wary eye upon the dark shape of the maneuvering *Alliance*. However, Captain Landais drew off, backed his yards, and seemed to be watching the two ships still locked in deadly embrace.

The broadsides of the *Alliance* also had done effective damage to the *Serapis*. And below, aboard the *Richard,* there came the steady pounding of Jones's emergency battery of three-pounders, which he somehow had kept firing from the poop deck. Jones himself directed this fire, aiming it at the mainmast of the British frigate. Then came a sudden lurch and the big stick swayed offside.

"Quick! Back to our own maintop!" As Fanning called the order he knew there was no time to lug back weapons and ammunition. The men would be fortunate to save themselves before the mast crashed. They must regain the main yardarm of the *Richard* immediately and hope that it, too, would not be carried away in the fall of the enemy's mainmast. His men had sensed the danger, even before Fanning's order, and they quickly inched over the safety foot rope toward their own yardarm.

The *Serapis's* mainmast trembled again, swaying so far that Fanning had to hold onto the yard and press down hard on the safety line to prevent being hurled to the enemy deck below. Somehow they all gained the maintop of the *Richard* less than a minute before the enemy's mainmast crashed, carrying away with it the top and royal masts, all the yards, and most of the mainmast rigging.

Chapter Eight

DANGEROUS MISSION

"Boarders away!"

Scarcely had he regained the maintop of his own ship than Fanning heard the cry for which he had waited so long. It came from his superior officer and friend, Lieutenant John Mayrant. The big French Huguenot sailor had been waiting all evening, Fanning could guess, for this chance. He wished he could slide down below to follow that daring sailor over the hammock nettings and onto the deck of the *Serapis*!

"Remember Portsea Gaol!"

Mayrant's fierce battlecry rang through both ships as cutlass and boarding pike were swung aboard the enemy vessel. To many men the slogan brought back bitter memories of experiences with the enemy. From below on the *Richard*

there sounded five sharp metallic strokes of the ship's bell.
Ten-thirty! The battle already had lasted some two and one-
half hours.

"Quarters! Quarters!"

Startled, Fanning listened with fast beating heart at the
sudden cry. It was the second time he had heard it that night,
but he was certain that this time it came from the deck of the
Serapis.

"The *Serapis* has struck her colors!" The cry was being
chanted by the men of the *Richard* directly below, but the
firing continued. The English gunners on the lower deck of
the frigate had resumed their sporadic cannon fire with
weapons that poked their black snouts through the portholes
of the American ship. The sharp rattle of musketry fire continued from the weapons of French marines aboard the
Richard.

Then, through the smoke, Fanning saw big John Mayrant
waving a cutlass as he leaped aboard the *Serapis*. Lieutenant
Richard Dale, first officer of the *Richard,* although badly
wounded, clung to the ship's rail, holding onto the main
topmast bobstay.

"The *Serapis* has struck," Mayrant quickly called to Dale.
"Stop the firing! Come aboard and take possession!"

Fanning turned to his men and ordered, "Cease fire!" The
men cheered. Captain Pearson of the *Serapis* had struck his
colors with his own hand. The gallant officer was unwilling
to sacrifice more men in the hopeless struggle. With his

mainmast gone he was helpless. Fanning's job on the main-top was done.

Captain Pearson was being piped over the side of the *Richard* with full naval honors when Fanning reached the quarterdeck, intending to report to Jones. The British commander, his uniform torn and battle-stained, advanced toward Commodore Jones, sword drawn. As he reached Jones, Captain Pearson reversed the weapon, extending it hilt first.

" 'Tis not without the greatest reluctance that I resign this to you, sir," Pearson said, "for of all the men upon the face of the globe, 'tis you I hate the most." The British captain's statement was made calmly, deliberately, but with no heat. It was a simple statement of fact. His feeling toward Jones was not so much personal enmity as for what Jones stood for—the daring success of the little American Navy and its allied privateers. But in this instance it had been the success of the *Richard* alone.

Jones, as all the world knew, for long had harried the very shores of the British Isles. Only a short time before the battle off Flamborough Head he had raided the estate of Lord Selkirk on the coast of Scotland, carrying away the much prized silver plate of the Countess of Selkirk. Jones later would return the plate to her, paying its heavy ransom out of his own pocket. But, at the moment, all Captain Pearson could see in the smiling, reddish-haired officer in front of him was the man who had mocked the British Navy. Jones had escaped after each daring raid to begin a new series of forays, and the English captain hated to surrender to such a rival.

Jones ignored the Englishman's declaration, but accepted and kept Pearson's sword. "You fought like a hero, sir, and I make no doubt your sovereign will reward you in a most ample manner for it," replied Jones.

Pearson ignored the compliment, asking, "What, Captain Jones, is your crew composed of mostly, Americans or Frenchmen?"

"Americans mostly, and some Frenchmen."

A thin, relieved smile broke out on Pearson's face. "Well," he said, "then it has been diamond cut diamond with us—a desperate family fight, brother against brother—for I must own that I think the Americans are equally as brave as the English!"

"Thank you, sir," replied Jones, obviously pleased, all the more because he saw that his opponent was sincere. "And now, sir, shall we go below to my cabin and arrange the terms of surrender? We had best hurry, for I am not certain how much longer my ship will keep afloat."

Within a short time the *Richard's* carpenters reported that not even extra men at the pumps could keep the ship afloat for long. There had been too many shots below the water-line, which could not be effectively plugged, so low had she been hulled by British cannon shot. The sea was gaining on the pumps by the minute.

Thus it was no surprise to Fanning when, as Jones and Pearson shortly came on deck, the Commodore called him over. Jones's orders were brief. The Commodore would go over to the *Serapis* with Captain Pearson and take command of her. He would hoist his own flag from her ensign gaff, rig a jury mainmast, sheer off from the *Richard,* and clean up the battered *Serapis.* Already the *Alliance,* the *Pallas,* and the *Vengeance,* the battle over, were standing by. They would send their small boats to take off the crew of the stricken *Richard.*

Midshipman Fanning, with another subofficer under his command and twenty men of the *Richard's* crew, was to remain aboard the sinking ship. They were to get most of the ammunition out of her magazine, load it into small boats, and send it over to the *Serapis* and her three consorts. The wounded men and the prisoners, of whom there were some fifty aboard the *Richard,* would be sent over to the other three vessels. Then, having executed these orders, Fanning was to abandon the *Good Man Richard.* All these things had to be done in a race against time. The pumps having been abandoned, the water would gain even faster in her hold. And there was more than the sea to be fought—fire had broken out in several parts of the ship.

By the time the wounded men had been transferred to waiting boats from the three consorts, with some from the *Serapis,* the fires were raging and the *Richard* had settled even lower in the water. She rolled sluggishly. Fortunately, the wind was light, but Fanning nevertheless realized that he had very little time.

"The magazine! The magazine! The fire is close to the magazine!" The cry of alarm came from a sailor who poked a grimy head sometime later through a hatchway.

The blaze proved to be small, but it had eaten to within a few inches of the magazine, where a considerable store of powder still lay. Most of the ship's remaining supply of powder already had been transferred to the other vessels. But there still was enough of the explosive left to blow up the *Richard* and her salvage crew unless the fire could be put out. Fanning, with the help of two others, quickly beat out the licking flames. This struggle took some time, and no sooner had he poked his head through a hatchway leading to the top deck than there came another cry of alarm.

"Mr. Fanning! Mr. Fanning! The prisoners have seized the quarterdeck and the fo'castle!" The cry came from admidship.

Fanning had removed the wounded men from the *Richard* before taking off either the ammunition or the prisoners. The wounded men needed immediate treatment, and there were surgeons aboard the three consorts. He hoped there were surgeons alive aboard the captured frigate who could help Dr. Brook, for some of the wounded had been sent aboard her. But in deciding the sequence in which to discharge his threefold orders he deliberately had taken a chance on what had happened.

Some of the prisoners had agreed to help load the ammunition, and they had been left unguarded. Taking advantage of the situation, they induced the others to help overpower the small guard detail. Evidently they intended to try getting the *Richard* before the wind, sail in close to shore, run her aground, and escape by swimming ashore. Once on Flamborough Head they would be among friends. The prisoners, too, knew that the ship was doomed. The chance was a desperate one, but worth the risk that they might be sunk by the gunfire of an American ship before reaching shoal water.

Quickly Fanning called all of his twenty men into the waist of the *Richard*. The Americans, he reminded them, possessed most of the arms and ammunition. True, the prisoners had fifty men to the American twenty, but they could be overpowered. He divided his small force into two groups, sending one unit forward under his second in command. Then he directed his own ten men to take what cover they could while stalking the prisoners on the quarterdeck.

There was plenty of cover, considering the littered condition of the deck. The sharp exchange of musket and pistol fire lasted only a few minutes before the prisoners suddenly decided to surrender. They had risked much to win a chance for freedom, but they were not ready to give their lives after having come safely through the battle. This time when the prisoners were rounded up they were placed in irons while awaiting transfer. Two of the enemy sailors had been killed in the brief encounter. Fanning sent all of them over to the *Pallas.*

Every one of his orders had been executed now, but Fanning decided to have a look around below deck before shoving off for the *Serapis.* Jones had instructed him to make a last check for papers he might have left behind. Fanning found a scene of terrible carnage in the gun room. There was not a piece of anything left whole. Blood was "ankle deep" and the "stench was horrible." The gun room had been breached so badly that "a coach and pair could have been driven through it from bulwark to bulwark," as he later wrote in his memoirs. There were many wooden splinters of all sizes and they, as much as lead pellets from muskets and cannon balls, had taken a terrible toll. During the action the enemy had thrown several loose cartridges into the gun room in an attempt to blow up the ship. He found that he had lost all of his personal belongings.

The ship canted forward at a steep angle and with each swell that raised her Fanning could hear sea water rolling heavily from one bulkhead to another in her hold. Suddenly she settled lower. A flood of sea water poured through her open gun ports. He must hurry to abandon ship.

The *Richard's* longboat, already manned, bobbed alongside in the rising swell as Fanning gained the ship's waist. Quickly he slid down the short distance on a rope, took his seat on the stern thwart, and gave the order to shove off. Even then he scarcely could accept the fact that such a gallant old ship was in her death agony, but he realized the necessity of getting away before she went under. Otherwise the suction might carry the longboat and her crew to the bottom along with the *Richard*. If there were any other papers aboard her, they would have to go down with the ship. Even to please the Commodore he no longer would risk the lives of his men. Quickly the longboat was fended free of the now badly listing vessel.

"Down oars!" At Fanning's order the blades went smoothly in unison into tholepins.

"Give way!" Blades dipped and cut the water. The longboat shot away from the *Richard*. And just in time! The boat was only fifty feet from her when she "fetched a heavy pitch," sinking quickly and silently into the sea, head downward, as a good fighting ship should.

The longboat's crew pulled in the night for the *Serapis*.

Chapter Nine

OUTWITTING THE ENEMY

Commodore Jones's little squadron, after making temporary repairs to the *Serapis,* hove to off the Texel Roads in Holland on October 3, 1779.

The *Serapis,* limping along for eleven days under jury, or temporary, masts borrowed from the *Alliance* and the captured *Countess of Scarborough,* had been convoyed by the *Vengeance* and the *Pallas.* The decks of all the ships had been cleared for action during most of their run from Flamborough Head.

Jones had been forced to seek a haven in a neutral Dutch port because of the still badly crippled *Serapis,* to which he had transferred his commodore's flag. She was in no condition to fight until she could get new masts and spars, new rigging and sails, and discharge the great number of wounded men who lay 'tween decks. There were so many of them that it would have been extremely difficult for the ablebodied men to work the ship's guns.

Sails of a pursuing British squadron were sighted now off the Texel Roads at the entrance to the Zuyder Zee. Time pressed if Jones were to avoid a battle that he was not equipped to fight. But the Dutch admiral in command at Texel Roads denied sanctuary for the American squadron.

Jones, with an anxious eye on the British canvas coming up so fast behind him, wasted no further time parleying with the Dutch admiral, but sharply informed him that he would sail into the Texel anyway and place his ships under the protection of the neutral Dutch government. That statement brought instant permission to enter the harbor, and Jones sailed into a neutral anchorage, under the guns of a powerful Dutch fleet, just in time to escape the British squadron. Since Great Britain and The Netherlands were then at peace, the British could do no more than cruise angrily off the coast. They dared not enter the harbor in pursuit, although they were no more than a cannon shot away when the last of the American ships reached safety.

As though Captain Landais had not done enough mischief, he almost at once challenged Captain Cottineau of the *Pallas* to a duel with swords and seriously wounded him. Landais soon received orders directly from Paris suspending him from command of the *Alliance*. For this dismissal he blamed Jones, and perhaps rightly, and challenged the Commodore

to a duel. Jones's reply to Landais' challenge was to order the
arrest of the French captain, but Landais escaped in the
night and fled to Paris.

Soon Jones learned that it was one thing to reach a safe
neutral haven, but it might be quite another to maintain
such a comfortable status while he refitted his ships. Sir Joseph Yorke, British minister at The Hague, the capital of
The Netherlands, demanded the surrender of the *Serapis*
and the *Countess of Scarborough* as having been illegally
captured in the battle off Flamborough Head. The Dutch
authorities undoubtedly sympathized with the Americans,
but they did not care to risk another war with Britain. And
since Sir Joseph threatened to demand his passport and quit
the country at once if the captured British warships were not
turned over to his government, the Dutch were undecided
what to do.

Midshipman Fanning, as Jones's confidential secretary,
was in the midst of the flurry of intrigue that went on for
days behind the scenes in the diplomatic battle to save the
captured warships and prevent them from being taken over
by the British. Then Jones, learning from a confidential
source that the Dutch government at last had decided to
yield to the British demands, devised a simple but clever
scheme to outwit both Sir Joseph and the weak Dutch officials.

Suddenly, on November 16, without warning, Jones transferred his commodore's flag from the captured *Serapis* to the

unquestionably American frigate *Alliance*. She was without a captain anyway since the suspension of Landais. Jones took his own crew with him, even though he had nearly double the rated number of men for the *Alliance*. He transferred Captain Cottineau from the *Pallas* to the *Serapis* and hoisted the French flag aboard her. She was now, for all legal purposes, a French ship of war, and the Dutch had no right to surrender her to the British as an American prize, since the *Serapis* fell at once under neutral Dutch protection. A French captain and crew took over the *Countess of Scarborough*, and she, too, hoisted French colors and so was under immediate protection. The British minister was outraged and made a terrible scene before the government authorities at The Hague, but he had been neatly outfoxed by Commodore Jones. The Dutch government was forced, quite likely all too willingly, to deny Sir Joseph's demand. Backing up this maneuver, the French minister at The Hague at once claimed both the *Serapis* and the *Countess of Scarborough* as French property and threatened to sever diplomatic relations if his demand were not honored. Soon afterward both warships sailed for Lorient, eluding the waiting British squadron, and arrived safely in port.

To the world, Jones had shown himself to be as adept in diplomacy as he was in the midst of a sea battle. But there was some suspicion as to how much Doctor Franklin had to do with the move. Nearly eight weeks had passed between the time Jones reached the Texel and the day he caused

French flags to be hoisted on the captured British ships. There had been ample time for Franklin to have received word of what was afoot and to have given secret instructions to Jones on how to outwit the British. Franklin did this sort of thing well; Jones lacked experience in such matters.

The incident was not only intensely interesting but most instructive to Midshipman Fanning. As Jones's secretary, he was on the inside of all the maneuvering, probably including whatever secret messages that may have passed by courier between Commodore Jones and Franklin.

Jones, after some further unpleasant experiences in dealing with the Dutch admiral, finally sailed from the Texel on December 28 in the *Alliance*, still with extra crews aboard— his own from the *Serapis* and the men from the *Richard* and Landais' vessel. After a short but uneventful cruise, his squadron dropped anchor in the harbor of Lorient in mid-February, 1780.

Orders from Paris awaited Jones. After refitting, he was to sail to America in the *Alliance* with dispatches from Doctor Franklin for Congress. There was Midshipman Fanning's chance to see his family and Betty Smith for a brief period, while the *Alliance* lay over at an American port, probably Boston, for repairs after her crossing of the Atlantic. He would keep his berth with Commodore Jones.

But this pleasant prospect soon was dashed by a bitter disappointment. Officers and crewmen of the ill-fated *Bon Homme Richard* had expected, after such a long delay, to collect their back pay at Lorient and their share of the prize money that the *Richard* had earned before she was lost. But the money was not to be had. There were many excuses by various French and American officials, but no payments.

Many members of the *Richard's* crew were in dire need, some of them having lost an arm or a leg in the battle off Flamborough Head. All needed new clothing. Fanning knew that the prize ships had been sold in France, and he discovered that the prize money was being held on a technicality by one Monsieur Jacques D. le Ray de Chaumont. At the first opportunity he determined that he would go to Paris and make a direct personal attempt to collect at least his share of the prize money. First, however, he had a job to do as secretary while the *Alliance* underwent substantial alterations. Jones had decided to take her over as his flagship, and he was refitting her from stem to stern, from keel to topgallant yard.

Work on the *Alliance* was being rushed, the more quickly to get the dispatches to America, and in a few months she was ready to sail at the next high tide. Ships sailed "with the tide" so that they would be sure to have deeper water under their keel when they cleared a harbor.

Jones was ashore in Lorient on June 23, 1780, having a farewell dinner with the French commandant. The *Alliance* still carried two sets of officers and two crews. Jones's officers were at dinner in the wardroom aboard the *Alliance*, early in the afternoon. Suddenly they were startled by three loud cheers in French from the quarterdeck. Almost immediately they were summoned topside and were stunned to see Captain Landais, in full uniform, surrounded by his own officers, all armed, with a strong force of armed French crewmen lining the rail and manning the yards. The vessel, Fanning could see at a glance, was in the undisputed possession of Captain Landais, although Jones was the legally named commander.

Landais announced boldly that he had taken over command of the ship and that such of Jones's officers as were not willing to accept him as captain would have to leave the vessel at once. There was nothing for Midshipman Fanning and his compatriots to do but comply with the order since they were not willing to serve under Landais. Fanning quickly carried his dunnage ashore, with the others, and they were forced to watch helplessly while the lines were cast off and the newly refitted *Alliance* cleared Lorient before a shot could be fired from the fort to stop her. Her American crewmen were forced to remain aboard by Landais' order since he needed them to work the ship.

Landais came to anchor under the nearby Ile de Groix, outside the harbor and safe from the guns of the fort, awaiting the expected courier from Paris with the dispatches for America. Jones, when told what had happened, was almost speechless with anger. Fanning feared he might have a stroke. To have been outfoxed by a man like Landais was too much, but Jones wasted no time on mere words and swung into immediate action. Although Landais' seizure of the ship virtually was an act of piracy, he still held his American naval commission and no one in France had authority to take it from him.

Jones sent small armed boats out to the *Alliance* to capture her while she waited for the American dispatch bearer, but they were forced to return to port when Landais threatened to turn his big guns on them. The slowly rising smoke of his lighted linstocks along the bulwarks of the *Alliance* made it plain that his cannon indeed were ready to fire.

Jones or Fanning would not have been comforted much could they have known how little this bold and mutinous action was to profit Landais. When he reached Boston he was arrested and tried by a court-martial aboard the *Alliance*. Landais was found guilty on several counts of breach of orders of Congress and breach of two articles in Navy regulations. The court broke him and judged him incapable of serving in the American Navy in the future.

Both Commodore Jones and his midshipman-secretary now had an important problem to solve. They were as effectively "on the beach" in Lorient harbor as any common sailor who has been fired from his berth before the mast. Neither of them intended to take this setback to their careers without a fight. Before another twenty-four hours had passed, Jones, accompanied by Fanning, set off to Paris to find a new ship and to collect prize money for the officers and crewmen of the old *Richard*.

This trip to Paris was more hurried than the earlier one,

but again Midshipman Fanning found himself sharing some
of Jones's popularity at court. Indeed, he was beginning to
attract more attention himself, thanks to an engaging personality and the ease with which he acquired the manners of
French society.

Jones was more popular than ever at Versailles, and King
Louis XVI presented to him an elegant gold-hilted sword set
in diamonds worth about $25,000 in modern American
money—a most handsome gift. It was, said the king, in recognition of Jones's bravery and resourcefulness aboard the
Bon Homme Richard. Queen Marie Antoinette invited the
Commodore to sit in her box at the theater and presented a
handsome nosegay to him. These outward marks of respect
from the sovereign and his queen enraged many French
naval officers then in Paris, but there was little they could do
but fume privately. Fanning, as secretary to the Commodore
and, in effect, his only aide, often attended the gay parties
and the royal audiences. Thanks largely to King Louis and
Benjamin Franklin, Mousieur Chaumont released some of the
prize money that Jones's men so badly needed. Between
them the French Ministry of Marine and Doctor Franklin
finally arranged that Jones should take command of a twenty-
four-gun frigate, the *Ariel,* recently captured from the English. The warship was refitting in Lorient. Jones hurried
back to that port and took command of her on July 15.
There was a big celebration, for the townsfolk were happy

that "the king of Brittany," as they liked to refer to the Commodore, again would sail against the English.

Jones cleared the harbor of Lorient October 7, 1780, convoying fourteen American merchant ships, with three privateers as armed consorts. At ten o'clock that night the wind suddenly shifted and blew a heavy gale. The *Ariel* lost contact with the merchant fleet and her consort privateers in the darkness. For two days she rode out the storm. Jones was forced to cut away all three of her masts to prevent her from capsizing. She limped back into Lorient a few days later under jury masts, temporary short spars carrying only a part of her sails.

By the time the *Ariel* was ready for sea again, some of Jones's petty officers and most of his crew were demanding more loudly than ever payment of the prize money they had earned while serving aboard the *Richard*. They knew Jones had collected funds in Paris. They needed the money, they told him, to buy warm clothing for winter service at sea.

Jones, greatly enraged by the demand, however just, promptly arrested the petty officers and had them clapped into prison for "impertinence."

Midshipman Fanning had accustomed himself somewhat to Jones's stinginess and frequent violent bursts of temper and brutality toward his officers. He even had forgiven the Commodore, during his service aboard the captured *Serapis*, for once having "kicked Mr. Fanning out of the cabin, across the deck, and down the hatchway," as the log of the *Serapis* shows, because Fanning accidentally had dropped one of the chronometers—an instrument used in navigation. But Jones's behavior was becoming intolerable. There was not only the imprisonment of several subofficers for "impertinence" when they demanded their back pay and prize money, after waiting for so many months, but the brutal manner in which Jones had treated a guest aboard the ship. He was a young man named Sullivan, who personally had been given passage to America by Doctor Franklin. Fanning's anger at last had been aroused. He was determined not to sail with Jones in the *Ariel* on her next cruise. In this decision he was joined by several shipmates.

Nor was it balm to their outraged sense of justice when, a short time later, the imprisoned petty officers were freed by a peremptory order from Paris; or that young Sullivan, when he gained his freedom and went ashore after being so long detained by Jones, sought out the Commodore and soundly thrashed him with a thick walking stick. The Commodore had refused to accept Sullivan's challenge to a duel and the unmerciful beating followed. Fanning decided to end what had become an irksome service. These incidents, too, had cooled the affection of the people of Lorient for the Commodore, although they still highly respected him as a courageous sailor. As a result, Jones had difficulty in signing on a new crew. In this emergency he did not hesitate to send out press gangs of his own, and he impressed into service aboard the *Ariel* crewmen from several American letters of marque then lying in the harbor.

Jones, however, still could be magnanimous as well as brutal, according to his temper at the moment. He was outraged when Fanning told him as tactfully as he could that he had decided to remain ashore, but his midshipman-secretary received a certificate of prize money due and a letter of recommendation for his services.

Then Jones sailed for America. His convoy of merchant ships lost all but two vessels on the crossing.

Chapter Ten

UNDER FRENCH COLORS

Far more than dissatisfaction and disenchantment with Commodore Jones had influenced Nathaniel Fanning's decision to remain in Lorient. No one realized more clearly than he that there was greater need than ever for bold Boston privateersmen, whether they sailed under American or French colors, for again the war was going badly in America. Every ship from across the Atlantic, it seemed, brought disturbing news.

General Horatio Gates, who had defeated Gentleman Johnny Burgoyne at Saratoga, late in 1777, had been badly defeated at Camden, South Carolina, on August 16, 1780 when he tried to wrest the South from the British. The enemy, who had shifted operations to the South when they failed to split the northern colonies along the line of the Hudson River, regained in a four months' campaign in the South all they had lost in prestige in the North. The whole South seemed likely now to fall to British arms, for Gates's defeat might be the start of a mopping-up operation of all the former colonies below Maryland.

British naval ships somehow must be diverted at once in large numbers from convoying troops to North America and from bottling up French naval forces and armies who had gone to America to help the rebels. And the quickest and most effective way to insure this diversion would be to put the British Isles' home shipping in greater peril than ever from enemy privateers. Besides, with the war taking an increasingly bad turn in America, no one knew at what moment the fickle King Louis of France might decide to withdraw his support from the revolting colonies—perhaps he even might make a separate peace with England.

This pressing need for even bolder action in European waters coincided with Fanning's own plans after leaving Jones. He began actively to seek a berth as captain of a French privateer, since there seemed to be no American ships available for that purpose. Among the many friends he had made in Lorient was Henri Bellemont, a wealthy merchant. Bellemont had a big share in a small privateer then fitting out in Morlaix, on the north side of the peninsula of Brittany. He urged Midshipman Fanning to take command of the vessel.

Fanning, having obtained a small advance on his back
wages and prize money from the American agent in Lorient,
settled his board and lodging debts, borrowed more money
from French friends, and armed with several letters of recommendation from prominent friends in Lorient, set off
overland for Morlaix. He arrived two days before Christmas
and was warmly welcomed. He quickly made new friends.
Monsieur Bellemont's associate owners of the privateer
agreed with their friend in Lorient that Midshipman Fanning, who spoke French so fluently, was just the man to
command the new private ship of war.

Morlaix, nestling on a river between high mountains, with
a fine anchorage, was well situated for such a highly secret
and dangerous venture. The harbor was protected from
winds blowing from any quarter and a strong, well-manned
fort straddled the entrance from the English Channel. It was
an ideal spot from which to make quick, daring raids on
British home shipping and bigger convoys from overseas.

The *Count de Guichen* was a sturdy lugger, newly fitted
out as a privateer. She carried two almost square sails and
two jib sails forward. She was armed with fourteen three-
pounder cannon, seven to a side—small of bore but adequate
for their purpose. Fanning wasn't sure that he liked the
ship's rig, for only in the Gulf of Mexico in the New World
was it well known, although it was commonly used else-
where. He never had sailed a lugger and her qualities were

yet to be proved. But his crew would consist almost entirely of Bostonians, with a few French sailors.

Fanning might have expected that things were going too well. On the eve of sailing, the marine authorities in Morlaix informed the lugger's owners that there must be a change in command. Orders had been received from the Ministry of Marine in Paris that only a Frenchman could command a privateer flying French colors and commissioned by the government. Fanning would have to accept the post of co-captain or give up the venture. The real commander would be a young French naval lieutenant, Pierre Anthon, who was on detached service from the French Navy. Anthon just had arrived from Paris.

The blow was a hard one for Fanning, dashing all his high hopes for an independent command. But, since he must, he made the best of the situation with his usual good grace, accepting the inevitable. Fortunately, Anthon proved from the first to be a young man of pleasing personality, good seamanship, and courage. The two young men had much in common. Fanning liked Anthon at once and the feeling was mutual. He felt that they would get along very well together as associate commanders. Anthon seemed to be somewhat too easygoing and lacking in aggressiveness for a privateersman, but since he spoke little English, they agreed that Fanning would give most of the orders and would be captain in all but name.

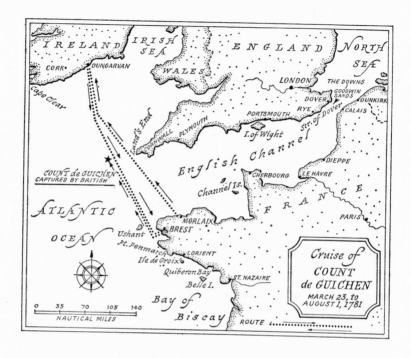

Four days out of Morlaix, which the *Count de Guichen*
cleared on March 23, 1781, Nathaniel Fanning braced his
legs wide apart as the lugger heeled hard to starboard. Sails
on her two masts caught the wind and sent her scurrying
southward in the Atlantic off the coast of Ireland.

It was cold on this late March morning, and he was glad of
the warm jacket and close-fitting cap snugged tightly down
over his hair. He eyed the four-sided sails and the slanting
spars and gave a little sigh of relief. Sailing the lugger, although a new experience for him, had proved to be a hap-
pier one than he had anticipated, for the little ship
performed much better than he had expected.

The squat, compact figure of Captain Anthon suddenly

emerged from his cabin and moved with a rolling gait toward the point where Fanning stood beside the helmsman on the little quarterdeck. Despite the division of authority, after only four days at sea, the two young men already were firm friends. For all practical purposes, indeed, Fanning was in command of his own ship.

So there they were, off the southern coast of Ireland, on a bright but cold morning in March, seeking valuable English ships to be captured and sent back as prizes of war to France. And keeping a sharp lookout for the fast English cruisers they knew were just as eagerly searching for them.

Fanning was in high spirits. For, much earlier in the morning, while Anthon had been peacefully sleeping on the off watch, Fanning, on his own initiative, had boarded four small enemy merchantmen with a single boatload of armed sailors and had forced the captains to make out ransom notes with a face value of 1200 guineas, or about $6000 in modern American money. Otherwise, he told the enemy skippers, he would be obliged to sink their craft with cannonfire. Also he had taken five hostages to insure payment of the ransom. This procedure often was followed by privateers when a vessel or its cargo was not worth sending home under a prize crew, but was of enough value to its owners to make payment of a ransom worthwhile.

Anthon reached Fanning and fired a quick, demanding question in French. Why had action been taken without consulting him? Fanning smiled, spread his hands in Gallic fashion, and tactfully explained that he had acted on his own authority because, since the operation was so simple, he had not thought it necessary to disturb the captain's rest. The real reason, of course, was that he had feared that if he did notify Anthon, his plan would have been rejected. Anthon would have considered sending only a boatload of men to capture the merchant ships too risky, even though none of the vessels appeared to be armed.

Already Fanning had learned that Anthon was deeply imbued with the policy that all too frequently actuated the French Navy—"to keep the fleet in being," rather than to take risks that could be avoided. This policy was directly contrary to both American and British naval practice, where risks were considered worthwhile if the stakes were high enough. Fanning and Anthon never would agree on this one point.

In this instance Fanning easily had convinced the skippers of the four small British craft that he really would sink them unless they complied. Anthon, satisfied at last with the explanation, shrugged with seeming indifference. He would not have carried out the operation that way, he seemed to indicate without voicing the thought, but he already had come to trust Fanning's judgment. And the 1200 guineas in ransom notes brought a gleam to the Frenchman's black eyes as he thought of his share of the prize money. He would have had to work a long time in the French Navy to earn as much. This reward was balm enough to soothe whatever prideful suspicion he might have had that his authority had been ignored.

The *Count de Guichen* was only four days out of Morlaix and already she had achieved considerable success, no matter to whom the credit must go. Anthon secretly admired the resourcefulness and the initiative of his young American associate, even though he may have thought Fanning somewhat reckless at times.

As for Fanning, much as he liked Anthon, he felt that the young Frenchman was handicapped by his excessive degree of caution, however great his personal courage. In the American service commanders had to take greater risks against odds. Having only a limited supply of gunpowder they had to depend mostly upon boarding an enemy vessel to capture her rather than forcing her surrender by gunfire. And, of course, Fanning thought like an American, even though he was sailing under French colors.

Fanning still deeply resented the fact that he had been deprived of outright command of the privateer because he was a foreigner in the eyes of the French Ministry of Marine. At last he had come to recognize the truth of what his friends, both in Lorient and in Morlaix, had told him, that if he would become a French citizen, even though temporarily and in name only, he would stand a better chance of gaining his own command. But he was not yet quite ready to make that much of a sacrifice to his pride as an American.

Suddenly there came a call from the lookout atop the lugger's foremast, "Deck ahoy! A ship, two points abaft the starboard beam!"

She was not quite straight ahead, a little to one side on the right side of the lugger, and no spy glass was needed to make out the stranger. An English frigate with a small cloud of sail spread, she was sailing west toward the Irish port of Cork. Soon afterward she was abreast of the lugger, her decks cleared for action, showing a twelve-gun broadside.

The lugger, too, was ready for battle, with all of her three-pounders loaded and run out. But the frigate foamed past, her officers seeming to take as little notice of the privateer as though the *Count de Guichen* had been a small and unimportant fishing boat. Fanning concluded that she herself was a privateer and that her commander deliberately was avoiding battle. Anthon agreed. Fanning gave chase, but when the lugger got within two miles of the enemy the frigate suddenly rounded to and fired a full broadside at her. The range was so ridiculously long, as the frigate's captain must have known, that both Anthon and Fanning concluded that the broadside was more an act of bravado than a warning or the commencement of an action. To them it indicated cowardice on the part of the enemy, especially since the ship was so much bigger than the French vessel.

"She's ours!" exclaimed Anthon. Fanning nodded, with a wide grin of anticipation, noting that the lugger rapidly was overhauling the enemy. The *Count de Guichen* was a faster sailer than the frigate since she could get closer to the wind, due to her rig.

"The frigate won't fight us," suggested Fanning, as the bigger ship rounded to again, still out of range, and fired a ragged broadside, the cannon balls splashing harmlessly far ahead of the lugger. Twice more the big ship rounded to, fired broadsides, then crowded on sail to escape.

"She's trying to scare us off," suggested Anthon.

Fanning grinned. "Only we don't scare easily."

Within cannon shot of the enemy the lugger ran up the French flag and, so that their foemen might know they had Yankees to fight, hoisted American colors, too. Almost always the English, Fanning noted in his memoirs, were wary of American boarding parties. There was great activity aboard the frigate and at last she appeared to be getting ready to fight if she must.

"Send our drummer forward to play 'Yankee Doodle,' " Fanning ordered the first officer of the lugger with a wide grin. Quickly a young drummer boy stationed himself with his drum at the head of the foremast. When the lugger drew near enough for the enemy to hear, the ship's fifer added the screech of his high-pitched instrument to the rolling cadence of the drum in a stirring rendition of the popular American war song.

Within minutes the lugger ran in under the frigate's stern and poured a raking fore-and-aft broadside into her. Then, passing across the enemy's forefoot, she gave her another broadside. But the frigate's gunners, too, were more accurate at close range, and they shot away one of the lugger's jibs and the foreyard slings, which tumbled to the deck, wrapping the drummer boy in billowing folds of canvas.

Repairs quickly were made, and lugger again got into position and fired another broadside, this time into the frigate's cabin windows. Then, luffing up under the enemy warship's lee, Fanning gave the order his men had been impatient to hear. "Lay her aboard!"

The two vessels were lying side by side, plank chafing plank, but before the lugger's crew could leap onto the frigate's deck, pistol, cutlass, and boarding pike in hand, there came a sharp cry from the quarterdeck: "Quarters! Quarters!" And the English colors reluctantly came inching down.

The cargo of the letter of marque, when a boarding party from the lugger examined her later, was valued at $150,000 in modern American money. Fanning put a prizemaster and thirteen men aboard and ordered her headed for Brest or Morlaix. Later he learned that she was retaken by the English, so it had been a futile battle.

Then the lugger's luck ran out, for she was forced to throw overboard most of her cannon to lighten ship during a violent storm. She was separated from her prize and later was forced to put into Brest for repairs.

The *Count de Guichen* was at sea again by April 7, 1781,

taking two prizes on the tenth, and the next day, off the Irish headlands of Dungarvan, taking three small sloops, ransoming two and burning the third. By evening she had captured eleven sail, ransoming all and taking hostages. Then Fanning spied two lofty ships standing before the wind directly before her.

Anthon would have run from them, but Fanning urged a fight. It was too late to escape anyway, he pointed out, if they proved to be English warships, and if they were merchantmen they might be captured and ransomed. The lugger fired a broadside into the nearer ship. She struck her colors at once and surrendered. The other was forced to round to and await orders from the French privateer.

Before the night's work was ended, thanks to Fanning's insistence that they attack, Captain Anthon had in his pockets ransom bills worth 10,450 guineas, or about $52,250 in modern American money.

But again the lugger's luck ran out. The British frigate *Aurora* captured her after a long chase, and Anthon and Fanning found themselves prisoners of war, with 10,450 guineas in ransom bills stuffed into Anthon's pockets.

Captain Anthon saved most of the ransom bills, despite a perfunctory search aboard the frigate. He did so by at once offering the British captain fake ransom notes which he and Fanning had prepared for just such an emergency. When exchanged, six weeks later, the two friends were able to start, in Morlaix, the machinery for collection of the face value of the notes. They had not dared to hope that it would be so easy to deceive the enemy.

Fanning took passage soon afterward from Morlaix for the West Indies, intending to return home to Stonington and Betty Smith, but the brigantine on which he sailed in July was chased by an enemy ship. She eluded her pursuer, but was wrecked somewhere west of the Isle of Bass, not far from Morlaix. Fanning lost everything—his small stock of gold and a modest shipment of fine French wines that he had intended to sell at a good profit in the West Indies on the way home. He arrived penniless back in Morlaix on July 17, 1781, discouraged but determined not to try to return home until the end of the war. Travel then would be safer and more certain. Whether he fought under American or French colors, so long as he saw action against the common enemy, made little difference, he decided. And, since he had so many influential friends in France, he soon might be able, through privateering, to recoup his losses. Sailing against the enemy, however, still was his main objective. But he would accede to the wishes of his friends—he would apply at once for French citizenship, even though he knew the arrangement would be only temporary. He would fight under the French flag again, but he would consider himself an American, no matter what his papers said. Apparently only in this way could he gain his objective—command of his own ship.

Fate, which had played such a shabby trick on him when

he had tried to return home on the ill-fated voyage, smiled again. Captain Anthon had learned that Fanning was "on the beach." The Frenchman wrote, in care of friends in Morlaix, offering him the post of second in command on a captured British cutter. She was then refitting in Dunkirk as a privateer. Joining Anthon would necessitate making a trip of 600 miles on horseback and by public coach, but the price seemed worth paying for the chance to get to sea again.

Within a few days Fanning set out, mounted on a good horse, provided with money borrowed from friends, and outfitted in new clothes. He reached the ancient walled city of Dinan, on the eastern boundary of Brittany, at the end of the first day of his journey. Then, by stage, he passed through the old walled towns of Normandy with their stone houses to Caen. The coach frequently was beset by hundreds of beggars, many of whom were victims of the crushing taxes levied by the king's collectors.

The countryside, in the late summer of 1781, was lush and beautiful. In Honfleur he ate "some of the whitest bread in France," baked in the famous ovens of the town. He crossed the swift-flowing Seine River to Havre de Grace and went on to Calais in Picardy. One last change of coach horses, and he was off to Dunkirk, where Anthon welcomed him with enthusiasm, and the two young men got down to the work of refitting the cutter.

Although he had applied for French citizenship, Fanning realized that the move would not help him immediately.

Anthon already had been appointed captain of the new privateer. Fanning would make at least one cruise aboard her, he decided, and then see what the chances were of striking out on his own.

The *Eclipse*, for that was the name of the captured English cutter, was, indeed, a "real beauty," as Anthon had described her in his letter. She was a staunch fighting ship, almost identical in her lines and rigging with the topsail sloops Fanning had sailed so often in home waters. True, she carried only eighteen six-pounder cannon, but by fast maneuver and surprise she might accomplish what she never could hope to achieve in a direct attack by gunfire alone.

With her fore-and-aft rig she could sail closer to the wind than a bigger, square-rigged ship. Hence she could sail faster with the wind on her quarter. And with her topsails and her mainsail she could sail at a good clip before the wind. She was sure to show a "pretty pair of heels" to the fastest frigate in His Britannic Majesty's Navy. Moreover, with her fore-and-aft rig she could risk sailing nearer to the land than the big square-riggers.

By December 1, 1781, the last barrel of powder and the last cartridge had been lugged aboard, the last water cask secured below deck, and the last spare sail and spar stowed away. The cutter was ready for sea. She waited only for the morning tide.

There was comfort for Fanning, on the eve of the voyage, as cheering news arrived from America. Word had been re-

ceived in Dunkirk of the surrender of the army of Lord
Cornwallis. He had been trapped by an American army and
a French fleet and army at Yorktown in Virginia the previous October. Cornwallis had been forced to flee from the
Carolinas to Virginia after a series of brilliant maneuvers
and hard-fought battles initiated by General Nathanael
Greene, Gilbert Fanning's commander in the Continental
commissary line of supply. Such a decisive victory as that at
Yorktown by the Army under Washington, with the help of
the French, ultimately would end the war, but at the moment the British still were resisting stubbornly in pockets
and showed few signs of quitting. At sea the war was being
fought with renewed fury. The need for French privateersmen was greater than ever. Indeed, apparently no matter
what might happen in far-off America, Britain and France
would continue their fierce sea war. They were fighting for
domination of the shipping lanes of the world, and no com-
promise in the rebellion of the thirteen American colonies
would end the rivalry of the two great maritime powers of
Europe in the near future—or so it seemed at the moment.

If peace were to come overnight for the United States,
there surely would be no berth for Nathaniel Fanning on an
American privateer, and the American Navy was so pitifully
small there seemed no likelihood of an opening in that service in peacetime. To remain in the French privateering service would be more profitable and much more patriotically
effective. Fanning had no thought, therefore, of returning

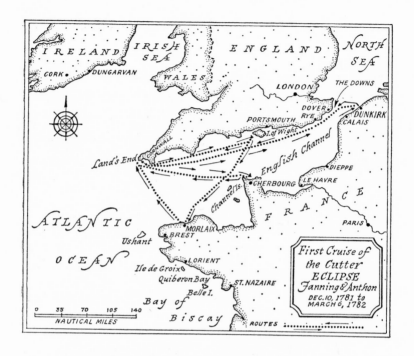

home until a general peace was signed by all the combatants.

The *Eclipse* cleared Dunkirk Harbor the next morning, bound, as Fanning wryly put it, "for a six weeks' cruise against the enemies of France and America."

The very next day she overhauled an eighteen-gun letter of marque and after only a three-quarter hour engagement in thick weather the enemy struck her colors. But when the fog lifted, a British frigate hove in sight and the prize had to be abandoned. Then, for days, while the *Eclipse* cruised off the British Isles, she alternately was chased by enemy frigates and took prizes, one after the other, sending them home to France under prize crews.

One day she fell in with a letter of marque mounting

twelve carriage guns. The prize was too much to pass up and, over Anthon's strong objections but with his final consent, Fanning had his way. He was determined to overhaul and board her. The cutter, fast with a newly cleaned bottom, gave chase. The enemy made a halfhearted running fight of it, trying to escape, replying to the cutter's bow-chaser shots with her own stern chaser. Neither ship damaged the other. Slowly but surely, after a while, the cutter gained on her quarry. Then Fanning gave the order that sent his men to the bulwarks and the rigging, armed with cutlasses, pistols, and boarding pikes. They were ready and eager to board the enemy.

"*A la bordage! A la bordage!*" shouted the French members of the crew, excited by the anticipation of hand-to-hand fighting. The cutter drew alongside the letter of marque, giving her a broadside of six-pound cannon shot. Grappling irons were hurled aboard her, binding the two ships fast together.

"Lay her aboard!"

At Fanning's shouted command all crewmen not needed to run the ship swung over the enemy bulwarks, some vaulting the rail and others riding over on spare lines from their own rigging. As the thud of sea boots pounded on the enemy's deck, crew and passengers scurried below for fancied safety. The English captain quickly doused his colors in token of surrender. His ship was found to be richly laden with textiles. She was bound from Plymouth, England, to

Saint Kitts in the West Indies. A prize crew was put aboard her, and she shaped a course for Brest, France.

The prize ship disappeared over the horizon, but the fortunes of the *Eclipse* took a turn for the worse. On January 3, 1782, a west southwest wind sprang up and, with her guns below for safety, the cutter stubbornly fought the gale for the next nine days. There were times when Fanning felt sure that she would founder. Only her staunch construction, aided by expert seamanship and bone-tiring labor, kept her afloat. Under nothing but a reefed topsail, to give her steerage way, she struggled until the wind abated somewhat.

When, with several rich prizes to her credit, the badly battered *Eclipse* put into Dunkirk on March 6, 1782, she was disarmed and laid up. She had made a good profit, but her owners were not satisfied with Captain Anthon as commander. Once her officers and crew were paid off and discharged, the owners were legally released from any further obligation to Anthon. He quickly accepted, and probably with considerable relief, an offer of transfer back into the regular French Navy.

Then the owners of the *Eclipse* offered to refit the cutter and give the command to Fanning. Word gets around quickly on the waterfront, and the sailors' talk gets back to ship owners. The syndicate that owned the privateer had learned what they suspected to be true—and the results of the cruise helped to prove it—that there was a big difference in ability and resourcefulness between Fanning and Anthon.

Anthon was much too cautious. Seldom was he willing to take big risks. Fanning, somewhat after the manner of John Paul Jones, shared the traits of ambition and boldness common to American fighting sailors. Many times he tactfully had been obliged to overcome Anthon's more cautious instincts when a rich prize was to be had with little risk. Fanning had been irked, but he controlled his irritation, and he sometimes acted independently when he had the watch.

A privateer needed just this spirit and daring if he were to capture enough rich prizes to make such a risky venture worthwhile for her backers.

Fanning at once accepted, especially when more than half his crew were to be Bostonians. Now that he was legally a French citizen he had more than half expected the offer to be made. But he had one stipulation, he told the owners. He had private business, in London, which should be attended to while the cutter was refitting. He intended to make a secret trip across the English Channel, despite the dangers of such a journey during wartime. They agreed, suggesting that while in London he should frequent coffeehouses and taverns—always places in which to pick up the latest public gossip—where he might learn something to the advantage of his owners. They were particularly anxious for Fanning to sound out English public sentiment with regard to overtures of peace between America and Britain if such should be made.

Fanning drew a letter of credit for 1500 guineas, about

$7500 in modern American money, from his French bankers on the London mercantile firm of Charles and Edward Hague. It probably gave authorization of payment of ransom bills for captured ships and cargoes. The Hagues would be reimbursed by the British government. Then Fanning was ready for his journey.

Chapter Eleven
SECRET JOURNEY

There was considerable danger in making a secret journey to London in wartime, but Fanning discounted it. Nevertheless, as always, he prepared as well as he could to meet emergencies.

Armed with his French bankers' letter of credit, safely sewed into the inner lining of his brown woolen coat, and a money belt containing a ready supply of gold English guineas, he felt safe enough. Warships of both France and England roamed the English Channel, but there were neutral packet boats making the run between Ostend and Dover, and they seldom were molested by warships. There was a certain amount of personal contact between the two countries, even in time of war, and the practice of nationals of one country or the other slipping across the Channel in a neutral packet boat was winked at by both sides.

At Dover Fanning hired a post chaise with four horses and was driven to Canterbury where he put up for the night. The inn where he lodged was crowded that night, chiefly because many persons had come long distances to witness the hanging of eleven English sailors at Deptford on the Thames. Fanning heard all the gruesome details from fellow lodgers while sitting before the tap-room fire that evening.

The tide ebbed and flowed in the Thames River with a fall of twenty-two feet. The condemned prisoners had been marched from the shore to a kind of wooden floating machine. There they were all put into close-fitting irons, which were affixed to their bodies, legs, and arms in such a manner that the prisoners could not bend. A halter was put about the neck of each. Then the floating platform, which had been especially built for the occasion, was towed off from shore under a gallows. After the machine was placed in position at high water, the hangman put each halter over the gallows and made it fast, leaving the men to die "at their leisure." Thus, instead of being executed at once, as when a trap is sprung, the sailors literally died by inches as the tide fell, lowering the floating platform. Fanning thought that this method of execution was the most inhuman of all.

Great Britain at that time inflicted this punishment upon any man caught under the American or French flags, if he

ever had been in the British Army or Navy and was proved
to be a British subject.

Next morning Fanning encountered another unsettling
practice. He had paid the Canterbury innkeeper for a night's
lodging and meals and was about to step into his hired post
chaise for the next leg of his rather leisurely journey to
London, when his host called him aside and begged for a few
minutes of private conversation. When they were alone in a
private room, the innkeeper asked bluntly if he were provided with guineas.

At Fanning's look of surprise and quite evident lack of
understanding, the innkeeper explained that the trip up to
London was most dangerous. Highway robbers might be met
at any moment. One way of providing at least some insur-
ance against too great a loss was to buy a quantity of counterfeit gold guineas. Then, if held up, the fake guineas could be
handed over by the traveler to the robbers. The highwaymen
would be in such a hurry to escape that they would ride away
before detecting the deception. Fanning's gold would be safe
in his money belt.

Startled at the man's suggestion, Fanning considered the
problem in two ways before making a decision. If he bought
the counterfeit guineas and was caught by the constabulary
on the way to London, he might be held, and even tried and
executed, as a French spy who had been sent over from
France to England to circulate counterfeit money. On the

other hand, if he should be held up and robbed, he would be in a sorry plight. With no funds except his letter of credit, he might be forced to disclose his identity, which undoubtedly would get him into trouble with the authorities. Either as an American and a rebel or as a French citizen he was an enemy alien and illegally in England.

The risk of being caught with counterfeit money seemed to be the lesser of two evils, so he bought twenty of the counterfeit guineas and the purse that went with them. He thought, upon a hasty examination of one of the counterfeits, that it was so well made it certainly would pass for a genuine coin, even to the sharp and practiced eyes of a highwayman.

The post chaise passed safely through Roxbury and approached a big tract of land, overgrown with a wild tangle of bushes. This spot, his coachman told him, with something like awe and a distinct note of fear in his voice, was Black Heath. The man seemed unashamedly fearful of what might happen before they had passed through the area. He whipped his horses to greater speed.

Suddenly, as the post chaise rounded a bend in the narrow dirt road, two masked horsemen barred the way and the coachman was forced to halt. Both the strangers were "very elegantly dressed and well mounted upon very handsome horses," and each was armed with a long-barrelled horse pistol. One of the highwaymen seized the bridles of the foremost horses, threatening to shoot the driver if he urged the animals an inch. The other robber levelled his long-barrelled pistol at Fanning's head and ordered him to hand over his purse.

Fanning at once reached for the purse containing the counterfeit money, feigning fear and great reluctance at being thus forced to part with it. The highwayman waved his pistol with an impatient gesture, ordering him to hurry.

At that moment, Fanning relates in his memoirs, there appeared just ahead a richly appointed coach and six, accompanied by several well-armed mounted liveried retainers. At this unexpected intrusion, the highwaymen abruptly "quit without the booty, clapt spurs to their horses, and rode off upon the gallop, struck out of the main road, leaped several ditches and fences, and were soon out of sight."

The coach and its guards passed on in a cloud of dust without stopping. Doubtless the armed men had seen the highwaymen, but the robbers had disappeared and there was nothing that could be done. The post chaise continued toward London, the driver quite evidently much shaken up and Fanning considering himself very lucky, indeed, to have escaped so easily. The purse of counterfeit guineas, however, still was an embarrassment, so, unobtrusively, as they neared the outskirts of London and it seemed certain he would have no further use for them, he dropped the purse out of the window onto the roadside.

Soon he could see the dome of Saint Paul's Cathedral, in spite of the heavy pall of black smoke that hung over the city in the thin, still air. Not long afterward the post chaise rolled to a jerky stop before the sign of the White Bear, in Picadilly. It was four o'clock in the afternoon of March 18, 1782. Fanning at last had reached London in safety, but he wondered what further adventures might lie before him.

Chapter Twelve

IN A LONDON COFFEEHOUSE

London's coffeehouses played an important role in the spreading of news and in the exchange of ideas. In almost any one of these establishments, at any hour of the day, a man could sit at a table with a mug of hot coffee or a dish of tea and hear the latest gossip, not only of London and the whole of the British Isles, but of the Continent and of far-off places. At this time the stalemated war in America was a favorite topic and the subject of hot debate.

London was tense with subdued excitement. The "peace party" had been a long time recruiting and consolidating its strength in Parliament, but at last, shortly before Fanning arrived in London on his secret mission, the friends of an American peace had gained the upper hand. Many of England's best officers had refused from the first to serve in the army in North America, and some of them had resigned their commissions rather than go overseas to fight the rebels. One of the most outspoken such officers was General Henry Seymour Conway. On February 22, 1782, General Conway had moved in Parliament against further prosecution of the war. The motion failed by one vote. Six days later, on February 28, a few weeks before Fanning's arrival, an even stronger motion was carried. On March 7 Frederick Lord North, the prime minister, resigned. Lord North had been the principal leader in the prosecution of the war. For months he had been growing unpopular, especially since the war had bogged down after the surrender of Lord Cornwallis at Yorktown the previous October.

King George III accepted Lord North's resignation on March 20 and named Charles Wentworth, Marquis of Rockingham, as prime minister. But William Petty-Fitzmaurice, Lord Shelburne, secretary of state for the colonies, was the real power behind the throne in the new government. Shelburne for many years had been close to the king, and it was openly said upon the naming of Rockingham that George III had made the appointment only with the understanding that foreign affairs, and particularly those relating to the American colonies, would be handled by Lord Shelburne. Closely associated with Shelburne was David Murray, Lord Stormont. He had been chief justice of England and was not only a famous barrister, but had been British ambassador to

France before the country declared war on Britain and sided with the American rebels. Both Shelburne and Stormont were close friends of Benjamin Franklin, especially Shelburne.

Some of London's excitement over these rapidly occurring events was reflected in the conversation in the coffeehouses. One evening in a coffeehouse that he had come to frequent Fanning heard a most enlightening conversation between two British colonels. The first colonel, who was home on leave after several years of service "in the colonies," described the ragged, ill-armed, underfed militia who had streamed into Boston to fight at Bunker Hill in the early days of the war and told of that brave defense and others equally valiant.

"Who," the colonel demanded of the other, who had stayed at home, "could have believed that these naked, half-paid, half-starved, barefooted rebels would ever have dared to face our regular, well-paid, well-fed, well-clothed troops?"

"Most certainly," replied the London colonel, "I never did believe it, and more, I never shall."

The overseas colonel shook his head, protesting sadly. "But it is all too true, my friend! They have often done it. And, besides, I could mention a number of instances where the rebels have fairly beaten our troops. And where numbers were equal to theirs, and sometimes superior. And of this you may rest assured as an absolute fact, that a regiment of these Yankee troops will always beat a regiment of British troops, provided that each regiment, British and American, consist of an equal number of officers and soldiers; especially when the contest gets to that pitch when it becomes necessary to decide at the point of the bayonet. I have had sufficient experience of it. I had enough of this sort of Yankee play at Bunker Hill."

He opened his ruffled shirt front and showed his friend where he had been wounded in the chest in that battle. "I have seen enough of the bravery of the Americans, so much so that I am determined after my furlough is out, if the government orders me to rejoin my regiment in America, to resign my commission."

His friend protested, aghast at such a brash statement. The overseas colonel declared, however, "We shall never be able, with all our fleets and armies, to conquer the Americans!"

"Hush, hush!" cautioned the London colonel, glancing around as though he half expected a provost marshal and a squad of soldiers to burst into the coffeehouse and arrest everyone for treason.

"I don't care," protested the colonel who was home on furlough, "who hears me! This is my opinion, and I will maintain it even in the presence of the ministry themselves!"

Night after night, for three weeks, Fanning heard conversations equally frank in the coffeehouses and in taprooms. Military and naval personnel, it seemed, were convinced the war in America could not be won. They were bitterly opposed to continuing the slaughter.

Thus far, at the end of three weeks in London, Fanning had escaped identification as either a French citizen or a native American—in either guise an enemy of Britain who might be treated as a spy if he were caught. He had completed his personal business with the Hague mercantile firm and that of his French friends who had entrusted him with theirs. He had soaked up about all the information he needed to confirm his belief that only a little push in the right direction would start a peace movement. While his luck still held he decided to return to France with his information. Perhaps what he had to report might help spur action on the diplomatic front, if his news could be sent to Paris.

Fanning left London at once, returning to France by the way he had come, and arrived back in Dunkirk on April 8, 1782, without incident—but wholly unprepared for the surprising news that awaited him.

Chapter Thirteen
"SOME PROPOSALS OF PEACE"

A meeting of the syndicate that owned the *Eclipse* was called secretly in the town hall of Dunkirk the very night of Fanning's arrival. He urged that word be sent to Paris that it was important to put out peace feelers, since the English quite evidently were so receptive. The sensational downfall of the North government pointed up the talk he had heard everywhere.

Now and then, as Fanning spoke, he could see a cautious nod or a guarded smile among the assembled, hard-headed merchants. He wasn't quite sure whether or not he was convincing them. But when he had finished his report, the stout merchant who presided as chairman reached silently for a sealed parchment that lay near to hand on the long, polished oak table. He handed the document to Fanning. It contained, he explained, "some proposals of peace" from the French court. These proposals and an explanatory letter had been received only that morning from Versailles by special messenger.

The instructions called for sending the document by a trusted courier to London. The courier also would carry private letters to Lord Shelburne and Lord Stormont. Fanning had the distinct impression, as the chairman of the meeting explained the mission, that Doctor Franklin had chosen him personally, if available, to carry the peace proposals to Lord Shelburne and Lord Stormont. His French friends did not say so, and Fanning himself later made no such claim, but he had known for some time that Franklin regarded him with more than usual favor.

The French court, however, had another errand for the special courier to London. Fanning was to carry letters from the king strongly urging clemency for two Irishmen who had commanded French privateers and who were on the eve of execution as traitors. Captain L. Ryan and Captain Mc-Carter were to be executed within a few days, probably on one of the infamous floating gallows that Fanning had heard about on his trip to London—unless Shelburne and Stormont could win the king's mercy. Possibly they might be saved, and they might even win their freedom, if the plea arrived in time. For England, while negotiating a peace treaty with America, would seek peace with France and Spain. The

Netherlands, too, had been at war with Britain since the end of 1780. Whatever small favors Britain might do for the French certainly could be expected to speed any future negotiations. Ryan and McCarter had become pawns in a diplomatic game of worldwide proportions.

Fanning felt a quick surge of pride in the realization that such an important mission had been entrusted to him—for that was the clear intimation of what the chairman told him. But he was trained to keep his feelings under control, so he merely accepted the document and the two letters in silence, nodding slightly in acknowledgment and waiting for further explanation.

There was none. The chairman merely asked him bluntly when he could leave for London. The men around the table had taken it for granted that Fanning would go. He did not disappoint them. He told them he could start at once.

So, less than twenty-four hours after landing at Ostend, Fanning found himself again aboard a fast packet boat, bound for Dover. But this time, instead of making the crossing to England as a private citizen of French naturalization, he was crossing Dover Strait as the representative of the French king and an American high commissioner to France. And one of the documents he carried could change the course of history!

He realized that his personal danger was almost as great now as on his first visit to London. For there was a powerful faction at the English court and in Parliament, headed by the ousted Lord North, still determined to keep the war going against America. Its leaders regarded the fledgling United States as "the rebel colonies," and the members did not intend that they should become England's "lost colonies." If some of these powerful men had even the slightest suspicion that Nathaniel Fanning carried "some proposals of peace" from the French court, he might expect rough treatment from their agents—even arrest and confinement in prison. The peace proposals would be confiscated and the new government in London would be ignorant of them. The enemies of peace were not likely to be barred from carrying out their plans by the fact that Fanning's letters were addressed to Lord Shelburne and Lord Stormont.

Shelburne and Stormont were as close to the throne as any statesmen could be. Few men in England, at the moment, would dare to dispute these two powerful lords or to interfere with a courier who bore dispatches or letters addressed to them. But Fanning realized that there were other individuals, still powerful, who were desperate enough to attempt almost anything—through their agents, of course, for they themselves would not resort to force. He had to be on guard every minute until his dispatches and letters were delivered.

Well before the little neutral packet boat neared the white chalk cliffs of Dover, Fanning had worked out a plan that he thought might give him greater assurance of safety and insure the delivery of his important documents. Secrecy had been his principal safeguard on the first visit; boldness would be his best protection on this second journey.

A customs man, soon after the packet docked in Dover, prepared to begin examination of Fanning's baggage.

"I am a courier for the French government," Fanning told the customs officer before he could start his inspection. "Do you think that, in the circumstances, you should inspect my baggage? I believe I am entitled to diplomatic immunity."

The customs officer somewhat reluctantly yielded, but he demanded proof.

"My business is with these gentlemen. And, as you may imagine, it is most urgent and requires the utmost secrecy and dispatch," Fanning explained in a confidential tone, as though sharing a well-kept secret. His accompanying smile seldom failed to win friends. "It would help me greatly if I could get on with my journey without delay."

The customs man carefully read the addresses on the two letters, shook his head in some doubt, then handed the missives back to Fanning, saluted and waved him away. The man had no reason to suspect that there was a third missive —the official peace proposals. The document might have brought handsome reward if it had been delivered into the hands of an agent of Lord North, so Fanning had kept it hidden. The letters were the reason for Fanning's haste. He had to get to London in time to save the lives of the two Irish rebels. They would die as traitors within less than twenty-four hours unless reprieved by the king.

Fanning hurried to the nearest inn, hired a post chaise and driver, and set off for London, offering the coachman the reward of a gold guinea if he made fast time. After reaching London in record time, he was driven first to the official residence of Lord Shelburne, where he presented the document from the French court and the letter asking his lordship's assistance in saving the lives of Captains Ryan and McCarter. Then he was driven to the residence of Viscount Stormont, where he presented the other letter in behalf of the two condemned privateersmen.

Time was precious, and both Shelburne and Stormont must work fast, cutting much official red tape if the two rebels were not to be hanged on a floating gallows with the next morning's tide. Only King George could save them and doubtless the monarch would have to be convinced of the expedience of acceding to the plea of the French court. But even George III would surely recognize the value of such a move.

Fanning had little doubt that the request would be granted, particularly after Lord Shelburne had read the contents of the document containing the proposals for peace. Shelburne publicly was quoted as still urging that the colonies be declared independent, but retained as a part of the British Empire. Any American proposals were certain to insist on complete independence and recognition of the United States as a sovereign nation, but at least a start had been made toward ending the war.

Shelburne and Stormont indeed worked fast, for in the coffeehouses the next day the talk centered only a little less on the publicly announced reprieve of Ryan and McCarter than on the rumors of negotiations looking toward an end of the war.

Fanning still had no official status, despite his bold assumption of diplomatic protection at dockside in Dover. But after a few days of remaining incognito he received "a kind of protection signed by Lord Stormont," as he afterward explained. Since Stormont was such an influential person, his safe-conduct pass should prove adequate. Doubtless another pass could be obtained from Lord Shelburne if it were needed, for he had been both courteous and kind and had indicated that he might have a reply to send back to Paris by Fanning.

Then, one morning, Fanning received a peremptory summons from Lord Stormont to present himself at his lordship's office. Stormont closely questioned Fanning regarding "a number of ransom bills, which it seems had been sent to Messrs. Charles and Edward Hague for collecting," as Fanning tells of the incident. Was Fanning indeed a French subject, his lordship wanted to know? Had he personally seen the signatures of English sea captains placed or affixed to these ransom bills, for payment of the captive ships' ransom? When Fanning, under oath, answered all of his lord-ship's questions in the affirmative, Stormont somewhat grumpily indicated that the amount of the ransom notes would be paid by the government. Fanning's own narrative of his exploits does not say that some of the notes that had been presented to the Hague firm for payment were his own, but he does add that "the amount of the said bills were afterward paid, as I was informed, by the gentlemen to whom they had been sent for collection." In any case, Lord Stormont would recognize Nathaniel Fanning as a French privateersman if he ever heard of him again.

There was time then for Fanning to relax and enjoy the hospitality of wartime London while waiting for letters that he might be required to carry back to France. Slowly the wheels of government were grinding out a counterproposal to that which had come from France. The government could not be expected to yield at once fully to the demands of the Americans. There would have to be much negotiation before a final peace could be hammered out.

As in Paris and in the French port cities of Lorient, Mor-laix, and Dunkirk, Fanning soon became popular among those to whom he was introduced. Edward Hague, who was an influential merchant and banker, opened social doors and made life pleasant for the ex-midshipman. Hague even lent Fanning his personal family ticket to Covent Garden The-ater. Drury Lane Theater, Ashley's Riding School, the Hay-market Opera, and other attractions drew him on many an evening. He attended private social gatherings as the protégé of Hague, and as usual he was popular with men and women alike. He always dressed fashionably, being now well able to afford the luxury and desiring to make the best impression. Life in France had given him a degree of sophistication and polish. The social graces, as well as the rough life of the sea, appealed to Fanning.

Within four weeks he was back in Dunkirk, his secret diplomatic mission accomplished, and itching to set foot on the quarterdeck of his own ship.

Chapter Fourteen

"CAPTAIN JOHN DYON"

On June 17, 1782, the topsail cutter *Eclipse* gently rode the chop of the North Sea off the Orkney Islands. She was eleven days out of Dunkirk, and Nathaniel Fanning was aboard her. These lonely waters off the tip of Scotland were good hunting grounds, but he had to keep a sharp eye out for patrolling British cruisers.

The newly outfitted cutter glistened with a fresh coat of paint, her rigging still smelled of newly applied tar, and her new canvas was spotless. Already Fanning had taken numerous prizes, including a cargo of fine Irish linen. The beginning was good, but he was uneasy.

The *Eclipse* had started this voyage with a complement of 110 officers and men, far more than could be easily accom-

modated aboard a ship of her size. But the extra men were
needed to provide prize crews for captured vessels. The result was that with so much less room aboard and so many
extra crewmen to feed, the cutter already was running short
of food. And he had no intention of putting back to France
for a fresh supply.

Just off the larboard beam, there now appeared a fair-sized
town, and he decided to lay over and take on a fresh supply
of whatever meat, poultry, and vegetables were to be had.
This visit might be risky, with so many British cruisers sure
to be nosing about these waters, and it might take a bit of
doing to fool these suspicious Scots, but he had to try.

Up went the English colors to the peak and Fanning sent a
boat ashore to demand supplies in the name of "Captain
John Dyon of His Majesty's Cutter *Surprise.*" This name was
the one he had decided upon to mask his real identity from
the British Admiralty. For if his true name were known, and
he later were captured, it might go hard with him. Not only
had he sailed with the notorious Jones, whom the English
regarded as little better than a pirate, but he himself might
have a price on his head for his captures in the *Count de
Guichen* and the *Eclipse.*

Half of Fanning's crew were Bostonians; the others were
French, English, Dutch, Germans, Flemings, Genoese,
Turks, Tunisians, and Algerians, all prime sailors with repu-
tations as stalwart fighting men. Here in the lonely Orkney
Islands his American seamen easily could pass for English, if

Second Cruise
of
ECLIPSE—
—FANNING
JUNE 6, 1782 TO END
OF AUGUST, 1782

ROUTE ....

0   35   70   105   140
NAUTICAL MILES

they did not talk too much. His English sailors could be used to carry out the masquerade. The Orkney Islanders should have no suspicion that his ship was other than she pretended to be—a British sloop of war. "His Majesty's Cutter *Surprise*" was as good a name as any. And there was certainly an ironic satisfaction in the name, for the cutter's real identity as a French privateer surely would prove a most unhappy surprise to enemy shipping or to these Orkney Islanders.

Fanning's demand for supplies was complied with at once, although not without some grumbling and haggling over prices, for the islanders were accustomed to obeying the king's sailors. A pilot was sent aboard and before nightfall the *Eclipse* dropped anchor in a small port that the natives called Hopes Bay. Here "Captain John Dyon" received a piece of unexpectedly good news. The townfolk said they were awaiting the arrival within a few days of several vessels from Quebec laden with rich cargoes of furs.

Ten days later, after vainly awaiting arrival of the fleet from Quebec, Fanning had about given up and would have left Hopes Bay when suddenly a lookout spotted two warships rounding the further tip of the island. From high up on his mainmast rigging he confirmed by the use of a spyglass that the alarming report was true. Two ships, indeed, were off the island. He could make out enough of the cut and size of their sails to be sure they were English. Apparently he was trapped, but he had two advantages: He was certain the townsfolk did not suspect his identity as a French privateersman, and the pilot assured him that the strange ships would not dare to venture into the harbor before the next morning. Wind, tide, and coming darkness were all against them. The entrance off this rocky harbor was too dangerous for an attempt to be made in darkness.

Fanning realized that he might have to fight his way out of the harbor next morning if he could not escape before his identity was learned. But suddenly he was determined not to be deprived of some compensation for the long and fruitless wait for the Quebec fleet. Indeed, he wondered if such a fleet existed. The town must pay a stiff ransom or he would burn it. This act, he admitted to himself, might not be altogether justifiable according to the strictly interpreted rules of war, but at least it would be some retaliation for similar actions by the enemy along the coast of the United States. He was particularly incensed by reports of the continued depredations of Captain Wallace in the British sloop of war *Rose.*

Fanning sent a lieutenant and a dozen well-armed men ashore with orders to demand a ransom of 10,000 pounds sterling, a little less than $50,000 in modern American money. The ransom would have to be paid within an hour or the town would be burned.

While the town magistrates were considering the demand, the lieutenant and his men, contrary to orders, began plundering the homes of some of the inhabitants and attempting to terrify some of the women. The outraged townsfolk arose in a body and attacked the would-be despoilers with clubs, rocks, and a few old rusty muskets. They eventually forced the landing party to retreat to the shore. At the water's edge the ship's company reformed and counterattacked. Fanning, not knowing how his men fared, but seeing the disturbance on shore, ordered several discharges of grape, round, and cannister shot. Under cover of this protective barrage the landing party escaped in their boat back to the *Eclipse.* They took with them much valuable silver plate and other booty, after setting the town on fire at several points.

The young lieutenant also brought back a beautiful, fair-haired young girl of sixteen. The lieutenant explained to the captain that he wished to marry her when the cutter reached France. He said he had brought her on board for this purpose and asked Fanning's permission to detain her.

Fanning was outraged at such a proposal, "and being," as he later wrote, "at first sight of this beautiful young lady, greatly prepossessed in her favor, and willing to restore her to liberty, and also knowing the lieutenant to be already married," he ordered the young officer confined in his cabin under arrest for "disobedience of orders, and for being so cruel as to bring off the young woman without the consent of her friends."

The girl was unharmed, she assured Fanning in her hard-to-understand Orkney Islands accent, but she begged him not to carry her away from her parents and to put her back on shore at once. Fanning instantly agreed to her request.

Putting the girl ashore presented quite a risk, for the cannon fire that had been needed to protect the retreat of the landing party surely must have been heard by the captains of the two enemy warships off the island. The sooner the *Eclipse* cleared the little harbor and got into the North Sea the better chance she would have, with more "sea room," either to fight or to run. And if the cannon fire happened not to have attracted the enemy, surely the column of smoke from the burning town would draw them into port with the first light of dawn. He had to risk a night run through the rocks at the harbor entrance to escape a possible trap.

Nonetheless, Fanning took time to carry out his promise to the girl. He was rowed ashore in the longboat and, despite a shower of clubs hurled by the townsfolk, he set her on the beach. He had written a brief note to her parents in which he assured them he did not war on women and children. What had happened was directly contrary to his orders and the officer responsible would be punished. The parents would discover that their daughter had come to no harm. In parting, he kissed the girl and she responded heartily. The townsfolk witnessed the scene in stolid silence, but there were no more stones or clubs thrown at the Americans.

The *Eclipse* was under way and her decks cleared for action by the time the longboat got back to her side. Quickly Fanning and his boat crew climbed aboard, the longboat was hoisted in, and the cutter gingerly negotiated the dangerous exit to the little harbor in the dark night. By midnight she "got clear of the Orkneys, without having run in the way of the two English cruisers."

Fanning knew the escape had been a narrow one, but he never did learn why the two warships were not lying in wait for the cutter off the harbor mouth. Next morning he was hunting prizes as usual. The *Eclipse* took two sloops, manned them with prize crews, and sent them to France. That night she captured four sloops. Three were sunk and all the captured crewmen were put aboard the fourth. Their captains signed papers saying they had been taken prisoner by the French warship and set free. The men individually also had to sign papers to this effect. There was a double reason for this procedure. Each prisoner was worth one English crown to a privateer captain, paid by the French government. And, for each prisoner so released, the English were in honor bound to release a French prisoner.

The *Eclipse* rounded the northern tip of Scotland and, a few days later, put into a harbor on the island of Saint Kilda. There "Captain John Dyon," his ship flying English colors, took on more supplies, for which he paid. But off the northern coast of Ireland the next day the privateer fell in with two English frigates. Before Fanning had time to maneuver out of danger he found himself being chased by both war ships. The enemy vessels were faster and were favored by the wind. Then fate nodded her head in the wrong direction. The cutter suddenly sprung the head of her mainmast. Thus seriously weakened she was forced to shorten sail. With the frigates directly to leeward, Fanning set his foresail and top-sail, and crowded on all the other canvas he dared and bore away.

One frigate soon was "as near as possible" to the cutter and the other shortly afterward tacked and "stood across our forefoot," crossing directly in front of the privateer. The British captains were maneuvering to block the cutter's escape.

The smudge from smoking slow matches on their linstocks rose along the bulwarks of the two enemy vessels as their crews stood to quarters. The cutter's gun crew maintained a stolid silence as they watched the scene, well knowing that within minutes they either might be sunk or captured.

"I was sensible," Fanning wrote later in his memoirs, "that I should be obliged to run a great risk; and for this reason, after the yards were secured with chains, as was customary previous to coming to action, I ordered every one of the officers and crew to lie as flat upon our deck as they could."

The men knew what that order meant. There was just enough open water between the two British frigates for the fore-and-aft rigged cutter to bear close to the wind and scoot between them. The maneuver indeed did entail a "great risk," for the little privateer very well might be shot to kindling wood between the broadsides of the two heavily armed warships. But if she could run the gantlet she might escape. The risk was, to a man of Fanning's kidney, worthwhile. And momentarily he succeeded in catching the enemy by surprise.

When Fanning's helmsman showed by his erratic steering that he was too much afraid to be trusted with the job, the captain abruptly grabbed the helm, shoved the man flat on the deck for safety, and, standing upright himself as he must, held a true course straight for the open water between the frigates.

This bold strategy caused only momentary confusion aboard the enemy ships. Almost at once they came about, thus somewhat widening the gap, and fired a broadside into the cutter, one on either beam. Musket and pistol fire raked the cutter from the frigates' decks. Round shot slugged through her mast, and the longboat, stowed in chocks on deck, was badly damaged. The main boom and the mainmast were "shot through."

Through it all—shot, cannon five, and splinters from boom and deck—Fanning held to his course through the narrow opening of water. Almost before anyone realized what was happening the action was all over. He had run the gantlet, and the cutter sped free into the open sea. She was pursued, of course, and the frigates kept their bow guns hot with firing at her, but all their shots fell short. Soon the *Eclipse* got so far to leeward the frigates were forced to give up the chase. Fanning counted his losses and found that, while several men had been wounded, none had been killed. Nor was any of the rigging damaged. As the wind was beginning to fail, the cut-

ter took the risk of setting more sail and, night coming on,
she got clear of the frigates. The encounter had been a close
call.

Some privateer captains might have decided to call the
voyage quits, but not Nathaniel Fanning. The prizes he already had sent to France assured the owners and all aboard a
handsome profit and their capture had made a sizeable dent
in the enemy's commerce. Since the British depended upon
their sea trade for a living, even in wartime, this achievement was a considerable contribution to the war effort. But
Fanning felt that he was, after all, seeking something more
than prize money. He was determined to exact as stiff a price
as he could on the enemy who had burned New London,
Connecticut, the previous September 6, and taken Fort
Griswold, on Groton Heights, by storm. Close friends of the
Fanning family had been massacred in the wild orgy of un-
disciplined killing that followed the surrender of the little
earthwork fort on the eastern heights of the Thames River in
Connecticut. The fort's commander, Colonel William Led-
yard, had been run through with his own sword when he
tendered the weapon, hilt forward, in token of surrender of
the little garrison to a Tory major.

Fanning's home town of Stonington was only twenty miles
away from Groton Heights, so the incident had burned
deeply into him when the report reached him in France,
many weeks later. He still had not quite recovered from the
shock of the burning of New London by the traitor, Bene-

dict Arnold, who led the British expedition from New York down Long Island Sound, and the massacre at Fort Griswold by the Tory major. Tories mostly had taken part in the attacking force, which eventually stormed the main gate and were responsible for the wholesale butchery that followed. Fanning felt that if, by serving under the French flag, he could harry the enemy that much longer, he wanted to do so. He intended to keep his private war going as long as he could, well knowing that peace might come any day and end his privateering career.

When, on July 1, the lookout aboard the *Eclipse* sighted a lofty sail to windward standing toward the cutter, Fanning ordered his ship cleared for action. He hoisted English colors. He could see that the other ship was pierced for twelve guns to a side, and they seemed, at closer range, to be nine-pounders. She was armed also with eighteen-pounder carronades mounted on carriages, with swivel guns on her bulwarks, so she heavily outgunned the *Eclipse.* Then, within gun range, he hauled down the English colors and hoisted the French and American flags.

The enemy privateer opened fire with a starboard broadside. Skillful maneuvering enabled the cutter, a smaller and faster vessel, to pour four quick broadsides into her.

Fanning's crewmen set up a loud shout: *"A la bordage, mon capitaine! A la bordage!"*

"Run her alongside!"

At Fanning's order to his helmsman, and even before the

two ships lay close abeam, the cutter's boarding party climbed onto the yards and standing rigging and onto their near rail, ready to swing aboard the enemy. Then a strange thing happened, but Fanning had seen it happen so often he was not surprised. Officers and men of the enemy privateer, seeing the grinning, half-naked Frenchmen and Americans and the motley crew of Turks, Algerians, and others, cutlass, pistol, and boarding pike in hand, fled their posts, threw down their weapons, and scurried below deck for protection. Only the enemy ship's captain remained on deck to strike her colors. Cold steel at close range called for a particular kind of courage, and Fanning's men had it in abundance. They would much rather take a ship by boarding than hammer her into submission by gunfire.

The enemy ship proved to be the *Lively Lass*, from the West Indies, bound for Liverpool with a rich cargo of rum, sugar, and cotton, and a crew of seventy-five. A provision ship was taken the next day and sent to France, but the cutter's mast and boom had been so badly weakened by wind, weather, and maneuvering that she was forced to put into Lorient to refit.

A complete overhaul required about three weeks. Fanning had competent officers to supervise the work, and the time seemed good to pay a visit to Paris and make certain that the *Eclipse* prize money and the wages due his officers and men would be paid on time. He had no intention of waiting for the slow machinery of the French bureaucracy for the settlement of accounts. Crewmen who are treated well by their commander, and especially those who are paid on time, are more willing workers. Part of his job was to run a happy ship. The only way to make certain the money would be paid on time was to go to the source, the French Ministry of Marine, with a letter from Benjamin Franklin.

Despite the tiresome and somewhat uncomfortable journey by coach, a few days in Paris, renewing old friendships, would be most pleasant and might prove profitable. There he would learn also at first hand the latest news from America.

The journey, of course, was not a new experience for Fanning, since he had been over the road with Commodore Jones, but he did not cease to marvel at two happenings that always occurred. The six-horse public coach traveled at what was then the madcap rate of twelve to fifteen miles an hour. There were stopovers at an inn for a change of horses, drivers, and sometimes the coach, every ten miles. Each new coachman, "as soon as he started his team on the next leg of the journey, would keep up a particular kind of cracking and snapping of his whip to denote that he had a generous set of passengers." But if the passengers did not tip the driver ten or a dozen sous before the start, the man would keep his whip socketed. This gesture silently advertised to the world that the coach carried passengers who were too stingy to part with a few sous to help out an underpaid and overworked public coachman. In this way he cleverly pressured customers into paying an extra fare, which, of course, went into his pocket. Always when Fanning rode the public coach there was an especially loud and frequent cracking of the driver's whip.

Inevitably, as the horses were slowed at the approach to a village, scores of men, women, and children emerged into the highway, sometimes almost blocking the coach and six, and all crying piteously for alms. Beggars of all ages were common in France, and Fanning had been told that their activity had been made necessary in many instances because high taxes had reduced them to beggary. Tax areas in those days in France were given to the highest bidder, or sometimes to the king's favorites among the nobility. A fixed sum went into the royal treasury. Then the purchaser of the tax rights was free to rob the public by levying exorbitant taxes. Sometimes even farmers or artisans who had saved up a little wealth eventually found themselves among the beggars, because after a time their homes and other property had to be sold to satisfy the greedy tax collectors.

Fanning could not help comparing this condition with that in his own country, where taxes were levied by the people themselves and on a more equitable basis. That principle, indeed, had been one of the causes of the Revolution, when George III and Lord North tried to levy taxes without the consent of the colonists. As on other occasions, Fanning had taken care to provide himself with plenty of small change to meet the demands of the coachmen and the need of the beggars. He was witnessing, although he probably did not realize it at the time, one of the pitiable conditions that soon would bring about the bloody French Revolution.

At Passy Fanning renewed acqaintance with the gentle-mannered but steel-willed Benjamin Franklin. One result of his visit was a letter to the French Ministry of Marine. When Fanning left by coach for Lorient a few days later, he had part of the gold due his officers and men for their courageous work aboard the *Eclipse.*

The work of refitting had been speeded up, and he found the cutter nearly ready for sea when he arrived back in Lorient. She cleared the French port on July 24, 1782.

Chapter Fifteen
HMS JUPITER

"Man the sweeps!"

Fanning's curt order sent picked men tumbling into the cutter's boats as they hit the water. Within seconds oar blades glistened wet in the late afternoon sunlight as they rose and fell with rhythmic strokes.

The *Eclipse* responded sluggishly to the pull of tow ropes in a calm sea. Gun crews were at their stations. She was three miles away from a British vessel across dead calm water off the southeast coast of Ireland on August 9, 1782.

Already on this cruise the cutter had taken several valuable prizes and sent them back to France. Now what seemed to be the richest prize of all lay just beyond reach, thanks to a sudden dying out of the wind. Towing the privateer to within gun range was dangerous, but the maneuver was the only way that she might get close enough to take her. Unanimously and with loud cheers the crew of the *Eclipse* had voted to undertake the dangerous mission, for Fanning would not order them to do it.

The sudden calm had left the ships out of range of each other's guns, and apparently the enemy ship did not intend to fight if she could help it. But stalking the quarry wouldn't be easy. The enemy began firing as soon as the cutter's boats pulled within pistol range. The Britisher, fortunately, was stern to the cutter, so she could bring only one gun to bear. These shots went wild, splashing up geysers of water but doing no damage.

By sunset the *Eclipse* had been towed close and was taking heavy pistol and musket fire. The privateer's bow chaser quickly silenced the lone gun the enemy could use effectively. Then, close aboard, Fanning gave his ship a "rank sheer," that is, he brought her squarely athwart the enemy's stern. As he did so he poured a broadside into her. It raked the Britisher fore and aft. In the resulting confusion aboard the enemy craft the cutter's boats towed her alongside the enemy.

"Lay her aboard!"

Grapnels were hurled to the enemy's bulwarks to secure the two vessels and in response to Fanning's shouted order the privateer's boarding party climbed onto her with wicked-looking, long-bladed knives. They were a particularly savage-looking crew this time, after taking turns for hours at the sweaty work of the sweeps. They were nearly naked, with wet, touseled hair. Rivulets of perspiration ran down their sooty bodies.

"We had on board the privateer about thirty of these boarding men," Fanning records. "They were Maltese, Genoese, Turks, and Algerians. They were large, stout, brawny men, and delighted in boarding an enemy. Upon these occasions they stripped themselves naked, excepting a thin pair of drawers, and used no other weapon but a long knife or dirk, which was secured in their girdles around their waists."

Five minutes of rough and tumble, jab and thrust, hand-to-hand encounter was enough for the enemy, even though, with many soldiers aboard, they greatly outnumbered the crew of the *Eclipse.*

"Quarters! Quarters!" came the cry. "For God's sake, quarters!" The enemy was offering to surrender to save their lives. Dousing their colors, all hands threw down their arms and stood with their hands high above their heads.

The ship proved to be a British letter of marque, out of Bristol, bound for Cork, laden with "the manufactures of old England." There were 127 British soldiers aboard, destined for Cork, where they were to join others, and then America, but they took no part in the fighting. Apparently it was not part of their job. The ship was sent to France with a prize crew, along with her prisoners. Perhaps the soldiers were just as well pleased to be out of the war.

Fanning was after bigger game next. Despite the danger of running afoul of the British Grand Fleet, he decided to cruise in the English Channel itself, so he shaped a course for Land's End, at the tip of the British Isles.

The *Eclipse* bowled along under a west southwest breeze that blew almost with gale force on the morning of August 11, 1782. Some skippers might have called his new plan foolhardy, and perhaps he was pressing his luck a bit too far. But if his bold plan succeeded he might be able to strike the hardest blow yet for the American cause in European waters. Any prize he captured in the English Channel, under the very noses of the lords of the British Admiralty, would give him even greater satisfaction than the prize money he earned.

Double lookouts were posted, and the men kept an extra sharp eye out for enemy ships. They, too, knew the *Eclipse* was in the most dangerous waters of her cruise. Anywhere between the Lizard, at the southern tip of Cornwall, and the Isle of Wight, across the channel from French Cherbourg, the cutter might encounter the whole Channel Fleet. The *Eclipse* was fast, but would she prove to be fast enough to escape any patrol craft that might be sent to catch her?

Every warship cruising in waters around the British Isles must have been alerted by now, Fanning figured, to be on the watch for "Captain John Dyon" and "His Majesty's Cutter *Surprise.*" They probably would not identify Nathaniel Fanning, recently a peace courier to London under the safe conduct of Lords Shelburne and Stormont as the daring "Captain John Dyon," the bold French privateer raider. But if he were caught, he supposed that he would be subject to a summary court martial and hanging at the yardarm of whatever British cruiser overhauled him.

Fanning's somewhat unpleasant reverie abruptly was broken by a call from one of his lookouts. "Ahoy the deck! Sail ho!"

Subconsciously he had been expecting the hail, and he automatically cupped a hand and called back, "Where away?"

"Two points abaft the larboard beam, sir!"

"Can you make out how many sail?"

"Three sail of ships, sir! Three king's frigates!"

Fanning reached for his spyglass, raced up the nearest ratline to a point almost halfway up the mainmast, then opened and levelled the instrument, studying the three ships. They were, indeed, king's frigates, and they certainly had sighted the *Eclipse,* for they were crowding on sail and coming up fast.

Quickly, upon regaining the deck, he ordered set every stitch of canvas the cutter could carry. Then he had the ship cleared for action and the men piped to quarters. Within seconds, at the boatswain's call, men of the off watch came tumbling up, rubbing sleep from their eyes. Cannon were run back on their carriages, the black-painted tampions, or wooden plugs, were pulled from the muzzles, gun barrels were swabbed out with sponges on long wooden rods. Powder, wadding, and cannon balls were rammed home within the muzzles. Gunport lids were raised and secured, and the guns were run out again. Gun crews stood by, the linstocks of lighted slow matches ready. The acrid smoke from them rose in smelly, smudgy thickness on both sides of the long, single gun deck.

Canvas men were at their stations, ready for any instantly needed maneuver of the ship when she came within firing range. No one thought she could outrun the frigates. The hulls of the big fighting craft loomed dark and sinister in the near distance. They were trying to come within effective firing range.

Suddenly one of the cutter's lookouts called, "Sail ho! Dead ahead!"

"Can you make her out?"

"She's a British cutter, sir!"

The *Eclipse* was making good time now and keeping ahead of the frigates, but apparently the enemy ship dead ahead deliberately was trying to block her escape. Fanning climbed the ratlines again and trained his spyglass on the foremost of the pursuing warships. Sure enough, flags were flying from her signal halyards. He backed down the ratline to the deck and, cupping his hands, called to officers and men, "We've got to take that cutter, men! Gun crews, stand by to fire!"

There was a loud cheer at the prospect of action. The cruise, for most of the men, had been much too tame, despite the many valuable prizes they had taken.

The cutter's helm swung over, and the *Eclipse* was set on a collision course with the British cutter. Already the two vessels were close enough so that Fanning could see the smoke from the enemy's slow matches.

That snapping halyard lined with signal flags on the British frigate had confirmed Fanning's instant suspicion: the cutter ahead had been ordered to intercept the *Eclipse*, and engage her if necessary, long enough to give the pursuing warships a chance to overhaul her. Perhaps he could outsail his pursuers, maybe not, but with so much metal against him he could take no other course. To avoid the heavier ships he had to put the cutter out of action and get away before the frigates could close in on him. Seconds would make the difference between success and failure.

Even so, the two cutters were within pistol shot almost before the *Eclipse* was wholly ready. Crewmen of the two cutters were exchanging pistol and musket fire. The vessels were sailing toward each other, bow on. Fanning waited, his crew expectantly silent, until the last possible moment. Then, as the *Eclipse* seemed about to ram the British cutter, he ordered his helm hard over, swinging the privateer squarely across the enemy's bow. Then he gave the order to fire.

The near battery of the *Eclipse* let go, raking the enemy ship from stem to stern. Quickly the *Eclipse* came about on the other tack, maneuvering as only a fore-and-aft rigged ship can be maneuvered in such a short time. Within minutes he was able to rake the enemy cutter with his other broadside. It disabled her. Her topmast, jib tackle, and peak tie had been shot away. The damage was not so great in itself, but she had been hit in such vital spots that time would be required to put her in condition. Temporarily she was out of action.

However, Fanning had lost precious time by this brief encounter. He needed no spyglass to tell him that the three frigates had come up much too close for his safety.

"Put her about," he ordered his helmsman, and the cutter quickly was got before the wind again. She scudded away under full sail. Soon, with the aid of his glass, he saw one of the frigates change course and go to the aid of the stricken English cutter. Some time later the cutter was taken in tow as the frigate headed for the nearest port. The other two frigates doggedly maintained the chase.

Fanning mounted the rigging, spyglass in hand, and for some time studied the pursuing ships. At length he snapped the instrument shut, nodding slowly to himself, and backed down the ratline. He had identified the foremost of his adversaries, the *Jupiter*, by her lines and the cut of her sails.

The *Jupiter* was one of the newest and fastest frigates in the British Navy. Already the other frigate was losing the race and dropping far behind. Mounting fifty guns, the *Jupiter* had not only more armament, but a far greater weight of metal than the *Eclipse*. Not even the most skillful maneuvering, plus the greatest amount of luck or bravery, could enable the French cutter to stand up to the pride of the king's navy. Fanning simply had to outsail the frigate or face the possible prospect of swinging from her main yardarm on the day of his capture.

Hours dragged by. The *Eclipse* and the *Jupiter* seemed to be glued to the waters of the English Channel. Save for the wind in the rigging, the strain of canvas, and the rush of water along the ship's sides, there was nothing to indicate that the cutter was in a deadly race for survival.

The ship's bell sounded. Three o'clock in the afternoon! Fanning reached for his spyglass again, climbed the nearer ratline, and levelled the instrument dead ahead. What he saw was startling, for some nine miles ahead, there was a line of sails stretching southward from the Isle of Wight. Blocking his escape was the whole English Channel Fleet!

The *Eclipse* had been neatly trapped between the chasing *Jupiter,* which so greatly outgunned her, and the Channel Fleet. Fanning counted the sail of twenty-eight ships in the grand fleet. Momentarily he was thrilled, despite his personal danger, at the imposing spectacle of the warships with their tall masts and wide spread of canvas. The sight was a majestic one. Thoughtfully he backed down the ratline to the deck.

"Take in our French colors," he ordered, "and show the English pendant." He hoped the trick might fool the enemy, but he expected no such good fortune, especially with the *Jupiter* coming up so fast. She would have time to signal the fleet. But what else was to be done? The *Eclipse* couldn't hope to make it back to a French port, as he had intended. Her only hope lay in somehow passing the Channel Fleet, running away from it and later trying to make Dunkirk or one of the Dutch ports, if he weren't overhauled first.

Quickly the French colors slatted down and the English flag was hoisted. Every man aboard the cutter could see that grim line of warships blocking the course of the *Eclipse*. They knew as well as their skipper that speed was essential in whatever order he might give.

"Every man who cannot speak English will go below!" Fanning ordered in French. "And every man of you will stay below until further orders!" French members of the crew sprang to obey, and the Genoese, Maltese, Turks, and Algerians, all understanding the order and the accompanying peremptory gestures, quickly followed. They could see how important it was that Fanning should seem to have an all-English crew.

Then came the test, and even Fanning, accustomed as he was to taking daring chances, felt a prideful thrill as the

Eclipse sailed with jaunty unconcern and foaming bow wave neatly between two hulking seventy-four-gun three-deckers of the grand fleet. These vessels were great ships of the line, powerful floating batteries that could battle with the toughest fighting ships in the world of that day. Either of the warships could have made kindling wood of the cutter within minutes.

There came a hail from the nearer of the three-deckers, "What cutter is that?"

For some reason, probably because the maneuver was so unexpected, no officer aboard the three-decker had spotted the French flag before it was replaced by English colors. Fanning was ready with a quick answer, and he fervently hoped that this British captain, at least, would not become suspicious at his reply.

"This is His Majesty's Cutter *Surprise!*"

Despite the tenseness of the moment, Fanning scarcely could suppress a chuckle at the audacity of his own statement. At the same instant the *Eclipse* dropped the peak of her mainsail and doused her colors, but she didn't shorten sail by an inch. She sped fast on her way through the whole British battle line, in a freshening wind.

Had his bold maneuver succeeded? Fanning wondered. He would soon know, for, glancing astern, he saw the chasing British frigate coming up fast. The breeze was adding to her speed. Then there came another hail from the three-decker.

The British officer's voice sounded faint, for the *Eclipse* was almost beyond hailing distance now. She was well through the line of enemy warships.

"Cutter *Surprise*," the British officer called through his speaking trumpet, "bring your ship to!"

This order meant that Fanning must drop his mainsail, back his topsail, lower his jib, and heave to while the enemy sent over a small boat with a boarding officer. It was what he had most feared, for if he backed his yards, lowered the peak of his sail, and rounded to await inspection he was all through. His ship would be seized as a prize of war, and he would be hauled off to a British naval prison. If he were lucky, he might not be hanged at a yardarm as the notorious raider, "Captain John Dyon." But this time, because he had taken so many valuable British prizes, and had caused so much embarrassment for the Royal Navy, he could expect no quick exchange, even if he were fortunate enough to escape immediate execution. He was one of the most sought-after Americans in the privateering service of either the United States or France.

"Aye, aye, sir!" Fanning replied smartly to the British order, using his speaking trumpet again. He took care that his reply should be loud enough to be distinctly heard aboard the three-decker. But the *Eclipse* held her course. Nor did she shorten sail.

Puffs of smoke at once plumed from three ships of the

line in the center of the fleet, but the cutter was out of range. The cannon balls fell far short, sending up harmless geysers of water that did not even wet the ship.

Then Fanning saw the *Jupiter* passing through the battle line. Three frigates, a sloop, and a cutter left the line, crowded on sail, and joined *Jupiter* in the chase. The *Jupiter* undoubtedly had signalled that she was chasing an American who previously had shown French colors. Every man aboard the British fleet now might suspect that the man they were after was either John Paul Jones or "Captain John Dyon." None knew him yet as Nathaniel Fanning or the ship as the *Eclipse,* but they would make every effort to capture him.

There was no course but to sail up the English Channel and hope the cutter's speed was greater than that of the pursuing warships. And the worst of Fanning's problem was that he had no way of knowing how many other British patrol craft might lie in wait ahead. He might be cut off before making the safe harbor of Dunkirk or one of the Dutch ports.

Chapter Sixteen

RUNNING THE GANTLET

Soon it was evident to Fanning that the second English cutter outsailed the other warships that had put out after him. She was more nearly a match for the *Eclipse*, herself a product of English shipyards. Perceiving her speed, he ordered his drag thrown overboard. This bundle of canvas, wood, and metal, tied stoutly and held by its weight beneath the water at the stern of the cutter, would permit the English vessel to gain more rapidly upon him. All the while he would seem to be straining with every inch of canvas he could spread to get away.

"Call the men to quarters," Fanning ordered, as the English cutter came foaming up astern. The Frenchmen, Genoese, Maltese, and Turks, who had been sent below while the *Eclipse* passed through the fleet, came tumbling up and took their assigned stations at guns and rigging.

On came the second British cutter. Her captain apparently did not suspect Fanning's trick. He thought his was the faster ship. Her crew had been called to quarters, and Fanning could see the smudge from their linstocks rising along her bulwarks. Soon she was within range and began to fire her bow chasers.

Fanning let her come a little closer, then suddenly he ordered his drag dropped, put his ship about and gave the enemy a full broadside. She had been caught bow on and took a wicked raking. Then Fanning came about on another tack and gave the enemy his other broadside. This time much of the British cutter's rigging was shot away, and she was badly hulled below the waterline. She would ship water fast and quite evidently was out of the fight.

Dusk had fallen and it was almost too dark to see, but Fanning was much encouraged by the fact that all the ships save the *Jupiter* had abandoned the chase. At last, she, too, seemed to have given up.

Toward midnight, Fanning went to his cabin and stretched out in his bunk for a brief rest. The crew, meanwhile, had made repairs, for the French cutter had been somewhat damaged in the brief engagement. Sail was shortened and the speed of the ship thus reduced. He did not want to get too far up the Channel during the night, since he

intended to make a dash for the French coast in the early
dawn.

Fanning, as was his habit, fell asleep at once. Just as he
dozed off, however, the slapping sound of a ship's bow wave
awoke him. He was awake, alert, and conscious of danger
without having to identify the sound that had awakened
him. The noise came through the open windows of his stern
cabin and could only have been made by the bow wave of a
fast pursuing ship.

He bounded from his bunk, peered briefly out of the
leaded window, but could see nothing in the inky darkness.
Still the hissing sound of the bow wave grew louder and was
unmistakable. The *Eclipse* was being chased and the pursuer
not only was close upon her heels, but was gaining fast!

Then there came, as though right from under the cutter's
stern, a sharp British order: "Strike, you damned rascal!
Drop the peak of your mainsail, hoist out your boat, and
come aboard His Majesty's ship!"

The *Jupiter*, far from having given up the chase, and favored by a night wind and the cutter's intentionally slower
speed, had sailed stealthily up the Channel in the wake of the
Eclipse. The frigate was within pistol range, but fortunately
she was not in a position at the moment, being bow on, to
deliver a raking broadside. If he obeyed her order to lay to,
he would expose his ship within minutes to such a deadly
maneuver and she would be helpless. His only safety lay in
flight.

Fanning sprinted to the quarterdeck and needed no speaking trumpet to call out a reply in the darkness to the *Jupiter's* commanding officer. His longboat, he said, was so full of holes that it would not float. The cutter's bell clanged out four o'clock in the morning, but it still was quite dark on deck.

"Very well, then," came the reply from the deck of the British frigate, "if your boat is unserviceable, we shall lower one of our own and board you. Show a lantern at your peak."

Fanning ordered a lantern hoisted to the peak of his mainsail to guide the British boat. Then he turned to his helmsman and ordered in a low voice, "Put her about. Smartly, now!" The *Eclipse*, with her fore-and-aft mainsail rig, came about easily even as Fanning heard the sound of oars in tholepins. The *Jupiter's* longboat was on the way over. He ordered his topsail yard backed, as though to lay to, awaiting boarding and inspection, for the light of the false dawn grew brighter now by the second and he could see that the *Jupiter* was taking in her upper sails. She was headed south, down the Channel, as she rounded to, ready to await the report of her boarding officer. Faintly now, in the dim light, there appeared the outline of the enemy longboat, an officer sitting stiffly erect on the stern thwart.

Fanning turned to his first officer. "Make sail!"

The *Eclipse* got under way again so swiftly that several

minutes went by before the *Jupiter's* captain seemed to realize that he had been tricked. By that time the cutter again was headed well north. There came a sharp order for the longboat to return to the frigate, and when the boat was out of the line of fire the *Jupiter* opened up on the *Eclipse.*

Fanning pushed his quartermaster down to the deck and seized the helm himself. "Down! Down, all of you! Lie flat on deck!"

Fanning was emphatic. Otherwise most of his men would have continued to return the enemy fire, and he had no intention of risking their lives needlessly in an engagement with superior numbers and firepower. First he must make a desperate attempt to get away at whatever risk to himself.

The *Jupiter,* which had been headed south as she rounded to, again slowly wore ship, but she could not maneuver as fast as the smaller vessel. Once around and headed after the *Eclipse,* however, she crowded on all sail.

Lead pellets whizzed over the deck thick as a swarm of angry hornets, and suddenly Fanning felt a stinging pain in his left leg. A splinter of wood, torn from the deck planking by a musket slug, had caused a painful flesh wound. But he scarcely minded the pain except for the initial impact of the splinter, so intent was he upon getting the cutter clear of the frigate. Then he felt a sudden pain in his forehead and knew that he had been stabbed by another splinter. The

Jupiter's main deck and tops were maintaining a heavy fire
of small arms while her bow gunners tried desperately either
to hull the cutter or to dismast her.

Fanning was stunned briefly by the shock of the second
splinter's impact, but he managed to hold the helm and keep
the cutter on course. She must be kept before the wind. If he
could put enough distance between the two ships, he could
set his stunsails and have a better chance to outrun the frigate. Moreover, such a maneuver would keep the enemy from
crossing his bow and raking him. It was better to die fighting
aboard the cutter than to take a chance on what the outraged
British captain might do to him if he were taken alive. There
might not be even the opportunity to appeal to Lord Shelburne or Lord Stormont.

Fanning was beginning to feel weak from loss of blood,
but he must hold the helm until the *Eclipse* was out of
range. Then he felt a hand on his arm and turned to see that
his first lieutenant had crawled over on his belly and was
reaching up to take the helm. Fanning shook his head at the
other's suggestion that he crawl below and sharply cautioned
the man to keep his head down, for the *Eclipse* still was
within pistol range.

It was almost daylight now, and Fanning could see that the
Jupiter was falling behind rapidly. Now it was safe for men
to stand erect again, and he ordered the stunsails set. By the
time the sun shone full upon the deck the *Jupiter* had been
left far astern. Soon thereafter he saw the frigate back her

yards, shorten sail, and reluctantly head into the wind and set a course for the English coast. At last she had given up the chase.

Only then did Fanning allow himself to be relieved at the helm. He went below to have his wounds treated and dressed, changed into a clean uniform after washing up, and ate a hearty breakfast. He was more hungry than he ever remembered being. When he returned to the quarterdeck an hour later, the coast of France was etched sharply off the starboard bow. Ahead lay Dunkirk, safety, and the chance to cash in on the rich prizes he had sent back to France—almost twenty-five of them! The *Eclipse* had come off well in the engagement, with only thirteen men wounded and none seriously.

But the cruise of the *Eclipse* wasn't over yet. At four bells, 10 o'clock, off Rye, England, the lookout cried: "Sail ho!" Within a short time the cutter overhauled a brig, laden with coal. She made no resistance and a prize crew was put aboard and she set a course for France, her prizemater being cautioned to keep well in toward the French coast on account of the English Channel Fleet.

Chapter Seventeen

A NARROW ESCAPE

If Fanning had been a cautious man he would have headed
for the safety of the nearest French port. But the lure of such
good hunting was too much, and he decided to remain a
while longer in these dangerous waters.

The cutter was off the Goodwin Sands in the narrow Strait
of Dover that separates England from France the next day,
after a thick and cloudy night. Scarcely had the bell struck
eight times, signalling noon, than there came a hail from her
lookout. A sail to windward was standing toward the *Eclipse.*

Fanning called his crew to quarters and cleared the ship
for action, but the vessel, flying English colors, passed within
gunshot without hailing. Perhaps it ignored them because
the cutter also flew the English flag. Fanning decided to find

out and ordered his colors hauled down and ran up the
French ensign. The enemy, seeing it, took in her light sails,
hauled by the wind, and stood for the privateer, her crew at
quarters, slow matches smoldering.

Fanning's own special crew of boarders was ready—French,
Genoese, Maltese, Turks, Algerians, and Yankees—stripped
to the waist and most of them carrying long knives and dirks.
"*A la bordage! A la bordage, mon capitaine!*"

Frenchmen of the boarding crew led the chant as the two
ships closed upon one another. Gunners stood ready, linstocks smudging.

Then came a hail from the English ship. She was bigger
than the cutter and carried twenty-four guns. "Strike, you
French beggars, or we will give you no quarters!"

With this command the English ship wore around and
fired a heavy broadside. The *Eclipse* staggered under the
impact, but quickly recovered and fired a broadside of her
own, raking the enemy from stem to stern, and doing her
more damage than the cutter had received.

Fanning felt a stinging pain in the calf of his left leg and
knew he had been hit by a musket ball, for there was general
firing now of both muskets and pistols. Quickly he tied the
wound with a big kerchief and kept his post beside the
helmsman. Already he could hear the groans of the wounded
and dying men aboard the other vessel, and, to make a quick
end of the fight, he ordered the privateer laid alongside. At
last his boarders got their chance.

The hand-to-hand struggle on the stranger's deck lasted
only six minutes. Many of the defenders were unnerved by
the sight of the lithe brown bodies and grinning faces of the
Eclipse boarding party as they swarmed over the rail or hung
suspended in the air, dropping down suddenly from ropes
slung from the yardarms. The enemy troops aboard the
stranger greatly outnumbered the depleted crew of the privateer, but there came a quick cry from the British for
"quarters" and the *Lord Howe* struck her colors. She was
from Cork, bound for The Downs, an area between Rams-
gate and Deal on the Dover Strait coast. The vessel was in
ballast with beef, pork, and butter, which would be useful to
the crew of the cutter. The remainder would be welcome in
France.

The prisoners just had been transferred to the privateer
and confined in the hold in irons when the murky weather
suddenly lifted. "Behold," wrote Fanning in telling of the
adventure, "an English frigate of thirty-two guns was close
aboard us! We were therefore obliged to abandon our prize."

Guns aboard the captured ship hurriedly were spiked or
dragged to her rail and tumbled into the sea; her colors were
hauled down and carried off. By the time the boarding party
had rowed back to the cutter at top speed, the *Eclipse* had
backed her topsail yard and her jib had been set. Even as the
longboat was being hoisted in, the cutter's mainsail was set
and she quickly bore away on a course for Dunkirk. But not

before the frigate had fired several bow-chaser shots, none of which took effect because the range still was too long.

Fanning knew that this time he really must put into Dunkirk, if he could escape that chasing frigate. With only 30 men of his original 110 now fit for duty—the result of sending so many prize crews home to France and his own battle casualties—and with so many prisoners and wounded men aboard, and the *Eclipse* herself badly damaged, he had no choice but to seek the safety of Dunkirk Harbor.

The enemy frigate had a far greater spread of canvas, which gave her the advantage. Fanning leveled his glass at the frigate. She was coming up fast. Suddenly he saw a sheet of flame rocket into the vessel's rigging. It seemed to have originated near her bow chaser, which had been firing steadily at the cutter. The flames spread rapidly, but he could see men beating them out, and soon buckets of sea water were being hoisted aboard to pour onto the flames. He suspected that bags of powder had been ignited by the careless use of a linstock.

The frigate yawed, her helmsman in the confusion failing to hold her to a steady course. She went off the wind and lost way—not for long but long enough for the *Eclipse* to put a greater distance between the two vessels.

The frigate regained her course, but it soon was obvious that she had lost so much time fighting the fire that she could not hope to cut off the *Eclipse.* Within minutes, on the next tack, the cutter sailed gracefully into Dunkirk harbor, braced her topsail yard, lowered the peak of her mainsail, and hove to, awaiting instructions from the harbor master as to where she should come to anchor. The chase was over. Accustomed though he was to danger, even Fanning felt that the encounter had been a close call.

Outside the harbor the British frigate majestically sailed past, as though tossing her head in disdain, and set a course back over Dover Strait.

The shoreline was black with shouting, cheering residents when the cutter dropped anchor. The crew set to work to make her shipshape. Wounded men had to be treated and sent ashore. Prisoners had to be transferred to the garrison dungeons under armed guard, waiting to be sent to a French naval prison. The deck litter had to be cleared up. But when at last Fanning and his officers and men could go ashore, they were jubilantly hailed as heroes. The reception was somewhat embarrassing to him, but he felt a tingle of pleasure all the same. The ending of the cruise had come close to being very different.

The story of the daring exploits of the *Eclipse* in taking so many valuable English prizes in waters surrounding the British Isles had preceded him into the French port. Hundreds of persons had watched the escape of the cutter from the frigate under desperate odds. No one ever had received a more rousing welcome from the citizens of Dunkirk. Bells were rung as though for a great victory, and for hours there came the steady, intermittent roar of cannon.

Nathaniel Fanning had been a privateersman in British waters for over two years, and this escape was one of his most exciting adventures. His career, however, was by no means over.

It was now the end of 1782 and peace might be proclaimed at any time, ending all privateering. Preliminary articles of peace had been signed at Paris on November 30. Fanning was determined to continue his raids as long as possible. Since the *Eclipse* was laid up, her owners planned to build a new brig for him to command. Meanwhile, after his wounds were healed, he bought a small cutter that he named the *Ranger*. At the same time he was given a commission of first lieutenant in the French Navy, awarded in recognition of his services to France.

With a crew of Americans, the little cutter cleared Dunkirk on October 23, 1783, setting a course across the Strait of Dover. The next day at dawn he found himself in the midst of a convoy of sixty British merchant ships. In one of Fanning's most audacious exploits, the *Ranger* joined this convoy, disguised as a harmless merchantman, and cut three ships out of the line before his identity was discovered. He sent these three prizes to France with their valuable cargoes. Then he was captured, but soon was exchanged and returned to Dunkirk on November 9, 1783. His share of the prize

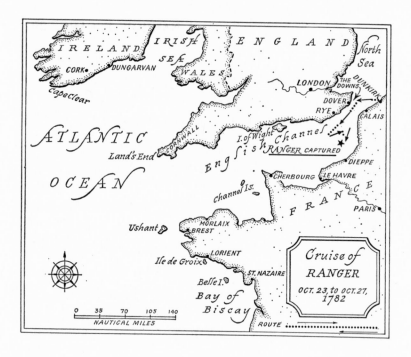

The following text appears within the map image:

IRELAND · IRISH SEA · ENGLAND · North Sea · WALES · CORK · DUNGARVAN · LONDON · THE DOWNS · DUNKIRK · Cape Clear · DOVER · RYE · CALAIS · ATLANTIC · CORNWALL · I. of Wight · Channel · RANGER CAPTURED · Land's End · English · DIEPPE · OCEAN · CHERBOURG · LE HAVRE · Channel Is. · FRANCE · PARIS · Ushant · MORLAIX · BREST · LORIENT · Ile de Groix · ST. NAZAIRE · Belle I. · Bay of Biscay · Cruise of RANGER · OCT. 23, to OCT. 27, 1782 · 0 35 70 105 140 NAUTICAL MILES · ROUTE

money from this cruise was about $5,000 in American money.

While still awaiting completion of the new brig, Fanning purchased a small, twenty-five-ton lugger, armed with only six three-pounder cannon, intending to make another short cruise. On the second day out, he was overhauled by the twenty-six-gun frigate, *Belle Poole.* Fanning had to surrender and was sent aboard the British frigate and sharply questioned by her captain, a man named Phips. For six weeks he was kept in chains, was fed nothing but bread and water, and suffered brutal treatment.

Half a pound of wormy bread and a pint of water was Fanning's daily allowance all the time he was aboard the

Belle Poole. The irons around his wrists and ankles were too small, especially those on his legs, and soon caused his limbs to swell, but no amount of pleading could induce any of the officers to replace the bracelets with larger ones. Instead Fanning was told he ought to be even more harshly punished "for fighting against his lawful sovereign" and for accepting a French naval commission. He was allowed nothing but the bare wood planking of the deck to lie upon, nothing for a pillow. None of the numerous American prisoners were allowed to come near him. He was kept constantly alone and not even members of the crew were allowed to talk with him.

Fanning does not say, in memoirs which were published many years later, that the probable reason for such brutal treatment was that he had been identified to Captain Phips as "Captain John Dyon of His Majesty's Cutter *Surprise.*" But for a long time every officer in the British fleet, and every common sailor, would have been on the lookout for "John Dyon," who had raised such havoc with English shipping from the Orkney Islands to Land's End. The British Navy would have been particularly incensed at the manner in which Fanning had "twisted the Lion's tail," to say nothing of the considerable number of prizes he had captured. The loss to private ship owners had been heavy from the operations of this one man.

All he could do for the moment was to endure silently the torture and wonder what might be in store for him when the

Belle Poole finally put in at a British port. At times he probably fully expected that he would be hanged either as a
traitor or as a pirate, despite his legitimate French naval
commission.

Then one night, six weeks after his capture, the *Belle
Poole* was cruising between the Isle of Wight and the coast of
France. She sailed by mistake into the very center of a
French fleet of twelve sail of the line. The French vessels
were too powerful for the *Belle Poole,* so she tried to run,
but in the end a French warship was too fast for her. She was
overhauled and forced to surrender. The French warship's
boarding party almost at once discovered Fanning, chained
between two cannon on the gun deck, and upon learning his
identity and rank struck off his chains.

Before daylight the French admiral, the Count de
Guichen, had been told of Fanning's sorry plight. He sent
his own barge over to transport the American on board his
flagship, the *Invincible.* When French officers had offered to
supply Fanning with a bath and a fresh uniform, he told
them he preferred to appear before the admiral just as Phips
had forced him to live for six weeks. The Count de Guichen
received Fanning kindly in his own cabin at the stern of
the great warship and asked him to sit down beside him and
relate his story.

Only then did Fanning tactfully call attention to the fact
that his ragged blouse and trousers were vermin ridden. The
startled admiral at once permitted him, before telling his

story, to withdraw to another cabin for a bath and a change of clothing. While Fanning was shaving, bathing, having his hair cut, and donning a clean uniform, the admiral peremptorily ordered Captain Phips brought aboard the flagship from another vessel in the fleet to which he had been sent as a prisoner.

Then, as Fanning relates in his memoirs, "as soon as I had dressed myself I returned to the cabin, where I found the Count, surrounded by several of the principal officers of the fleet, among whom I saw the English captain, who looked very sad. I was then requested by the admiral to be seated and relate the usage which I had received from the English.

"The admiral then told me that whatever the English captain had done with me while on board of the ship which he commanded, I had now his permission to order inflicted upon the captain. I did not, upon reflection, make any use of the permission granted me by the admiral, and thus (he) went unpunished for his barbarous and cruel usage inflicted upon me. But the Count ordered him to restore to me all the effects which had been taken from me by himself, his officers, or any of the ship's crew; and in default thereof, he was ordered to pay me the money to the amount of such effects, or so much as was missing; all of which was strictly complied with on the part of the English captain."

Admiral de Guichen ordered Fanning to duty aboard the flagship in his rank of Franch naval lieutenant during the

remainder of the cruise in the English Channel. The French
fleet during this cruise captured several enemy frigates,
sloops of war, and merchantmen. Then, after many months,
the warships put into Brest. Almost at once Fanning heard
that a general peace was expected to be proclaimed within
two months.

Admiral de Guichen graciously gave Fanning permission
to hurry back to Dunkirk at once. There it might be possible
to get in a few more weeks of privateering before a proclama-
tion of peace put an end to this form of adventure.

Back in Dunkirk he found the new brig, as yet unnamed,
nearly ready for sea. But it would be a race against time to
get her started on even a short cruise before the final peace
treaty signed in Paris on September 3, 1783, should be rati-
fied by all the signers and become effective. Fanning questioned whether he would get to sea in time.

At last the new brig was ready to sail with the tide on
December 30, 1783. Fanning ordered her lines cast off and
she floated free in the light harbor swell. He was about to
give the order to "make sail" for the open sea when there
came a loud pealing of bells. Cannon roared from the
ramparts of the fort guarding Dunkirk harbor. He could
hear wild cheering from the town. Then he spied a man in
uniform running down the quay gesticulating wildly.

The man proved to be an officer attached to the Ministry of Marine. He ordered Fanning to warp the brig back
alongside the quay. Peace, the officer explained, had been

proclaimed. The news had reached Dunkirk by fast courier only a few minutes before. Nathaniel Fanning's career as a privateersman had come to an abrupt but not unexpected end.

Fanning reacted almost as jubilantly as the townsfolk, but suddenly he felt war weary. There were no more sea battles to be fought, no more rich prizes to be captured. The long, hard-fought war for American independence had been won, not only on the battlefield but at the peace table. And he had achieved his own mission—to fight for his country in the only way in which he had been trained, upon the sea, and under conditions of his own choice. He had proved his courage and his ability as a privateer captain off the enemy's own coast. He had captured a total of fifty-two enemy ships in a privateering career lasting a few days more than three years. And he had acted as a special courier in carrying the first proposals of peace from Paris to London. His service had been a worthwhile achievement.

All at once, amid the roar of celebrating cannon and the pealing of jubilant bells, he felt a great longing for his native land and for a sight of the clear waters of Stonington Harbor. He had been away from home more than five years. Had Betty Smith waited for him? Of course, there was no reason why she should have. Other eligible young men in Stonington and nearby towns surely would have asked her to marry them. There was only one way to find out—that was to go home and ask her.

AFTERWORD

Fanning's was a wonderful homecoming.

Betty Smith had grown into a most attractive young woman, with kind, understanding eyes. In the years he had been away she had fulfilled all the promise of fifteen, her age when he sailed off to war. Best of all, he soon learned that she had not accepted any of the proposals of marriage made to her by young men of Stonington who had courted her.

Fanning and Betty Smith were married, after a brief courtship, on November 21, 1784, and went to live in a house on Long Point in Stonington. He settled down to the less exciting but still romantic business of merchant shipping. Part of the time for the next twenty years Fanning lived in Stonington, part of the time in New York.

But on May 1, 1801, the Dey of Algiers declared open war
on the United States. The declaration was only public recognition of a condition that had existed for a long time.
American merchant ships had been the prey of these ruthless
corsairs of the North African coast for years. Some European
maritime nations, including Great Britain, paid tribute to
these brutal pirates, but the United States refused to pay.

The resulting war with the Barbary Pirates, as they were
called, compelled the United States to start at once the build-
ing of a bigger and much stronger Navy. The country under-
took what today we would call a "crash program." Officers
were badly needed—men trained to command warships. For
many years almost every merchant ship had gone to sea
armed against pirates, especially when sailing to the far East
and the Mediterranean Sea, but officers trained in the art of
war were scarce.

With each passing month, men with naval or privateering
experience were in even greater demand. The naval establish-
ment called Nathaniel Fanning back to duty. He responded at
once and was commissioned a lieutenant in the United States
Navy on December 5, 1804. At first he was assigned to the
command of a gunboat. Within a short time he was transferred from a ship's deck to command the United States
Naval Station at Charleston, South Carolina. While on duty
in that port he was stricken with yellow fever and died on
September 30, 1805.

What Nathaniel Fanning's naval career might have been,

had he lived to participate in the War of 1812 against Great Britain we can only conjecture. Undoubtedly, because of his love for the sea and his exceptional experience, he would have risen to important command in the Navy. Or he might have returned to his old career of privateering, at which he had been so successful.

GLOSSARY OF SEA TERMS

AFT (or ABAFT)—Toward the stern.

ABEAM—Opposite middle part of ship's side.

BACK HER SAILS—To swing yards left, slowing or halting ship.

BACK HER YARDS—Shift yards to left.

BOBSTAY—Bowsprit stay.

BRING ABOUT—To change the tack.

EIGHT BELLS—Four, eight, or twelve o'clock.

FORECASTLE—Forward, crew's quarters.

FORE-AND-AFT RIG—Sails that pivot around mast.

FOREFOOT—Foremost part of ship's keel.

FORETOP—Top of foremast.

FORWARD—Toward the bow.

FRIGATE—Fast, three-masted sailing warship.

HALYARD—A line for hoisting sail, yard, or flag.

HARD BY THE WIND—Closer to the wind.

HOVE TO—Ship stopped.

JIBBOOM—Bowsprit spar.

JIB SAIL—Sail set on a boom.

JIBSTAY—Line holding a jib sail.

LARBOARD (PORT)—Left side of a ship.

LEE—Side away from the wind.

LUFF—To sail nearer to the wind or forward edge of fore-and-aft sail.

MAINSAIL—Principal sail on mainmast.

MAINSHEET—Line controlling main sail.

MAINTOP—Top of mainmast.

MIZZEN—Rear mast on three-masted ship.

PEAK—Outer, upper corner of a sail.

POOP—Stern deck.

QUARTERDECK—Promenade deck for officers.

RATLINE—Rope ladder rung between shrouds.

RAZEE—Ship with deck cut down.

SHROUD—Rope or wire supporting mast.

STARBOARD—Right side of ship.

STUNSAIL—Light sail set at end of spar.

TACK—To change course by shifting sail.

TRICE UP—To pull and tie up (as boarding net).

WATCH—Unit of ship's crew.

WEAR AROUND—To swing away from wind.

WAIST—Middle section of ship's deck.

WINDWARD—Toward the wind.

YAW—To lose way.

BIBLIOGRAPHY

Alden, John Richard, *The American Revolution: 1775–1783*. New York: Harper and Row, 1954.

Augur, Helen, *The Secret War of Independence*. New York: Duell, Sloan & Pearce, Inc., 1955.

Bailey, Luella H., (Private Papers), East Greenwich, Rhode Island, about 1900.

Barnes, John H., Lieutenant Commander USN, editor and annotator, *Fanning's Narrative, Memoirs of An American Naval Officer, 1778–1783*. (From an original manuscript by Nathaniel Fanning entitled, Memoirs of Captain Nathaniel Fanning, an American Naval Officer Who Served During Part of the American Revolution Under the Command of John Paul Jones, Esq. and Who Lately Died at Charleston in the Service of the United States. New York: 1808.) (Private Limited Edition)

Brooks, Walter F., *History of the Fanning Family*, Vol. II. Worcester, Massachusetts: Privately printed for the compiler, 1905.

Buell, A. C., *John Paul Jones, Founder of the American Navy*. 2 vols. New York: Charles Scribner's Sons, 1900.

Burke, Sir John Bernard, *A Genealogical and Heraldic Dictionary of the Peerage and Baronetage of the British Empire*. London: Hurst and Blackett, 1853.

Chapelle, Howard I., *History of the American Sailing Navy*. New York: W. W. Norton and Company, Inc., 1949.

Crane, Verner W., *Benjamin Franklin and a Rising People*. Boston: Little, Brown and Company, 1954.

Crawford, M. MacDermont, *John Paul Jones, The Sailor Whom England Feared*. New York: Duffield, 1913.

DeKoven, Anna (Farwell), *Life and Letters of John Paul Jones*. New York: Charles Scribner's Sons, 1913.

Donovan, Frank, selected, edited, and interpreted by, *The Benjamin Franklin Papers*. New York: Dodd, Mead and Company, 1962.

Dupuy, R. Ernest and Trevor N., *The Compact History of the Revolutionary War*. New York: Hawthorn Books, Inc., 1963.

Einstein, Lewis, *Divided Loyalties*. Boston: Houghton Mifflin Company, 1933.

Fanning, Edmund, *Voyages and Discoveries in the South Seas, 1792–1832, by Captain Edmund Fanning*. Salem, Massachusetts: Marine Research Society, 1924. (First published in 1833 under the title *Voyage Around the World,* and in 1838 under the title *Voyage to the South Seas.*)

Forbes, Allan, *Taverns and Stagecoaches of New England*, R. M. Eastman, editor. Boston: State Street Trust Company, 1953–54.

Freeman, Douglas Southall, *George Washington*, Vol. V. New York: Charles Scribner's Sons, 1952.

Greene, Francis Vinton, *Nathanael Greene*. New York: D. Appleton and Company, 1893.

Hill, Frederick Stanhope, *Romance of the American Navy*. New York: G. P. Putnam's Sons, 1910.

Knox, Captain Dudley Wright, U.S.N., *A History of the United States Navy*. New York: G. P. Putnam's Sons, 1936.

Lorenz, Lincoln, *John Paul Jones*. Annapolis: U.S. Naval Institute, 1943.

Mahan, Alfred Thayer, Admiral, U.S.N., *The Influence of Sea Power Upon History, 1660–1783*. Boston: Little, Brown and Company, 1890.

Morison, Samuel Eliot, *John Paul Jones*. Boston: Little, Brown and Company, 1959.

Morris, Richard B., *The Peacemakers*. New York: Harper & Row, 1965.

Paullin, C. O., "Admiral Pierre Landais." *Catholic Historical Review*, 17: 296–307, October, 1931.

Rogers, Ernest E., *Sesquecentennial of the Battle of Groton Heights and Burning of New London*. New London, Connecticut: Published for the Fort Griswold and Groton Monument Association, 1931.

Sprout, Harold and Margaret, *The Rise of American Naval Power*. Princeton: Princeton University Press, 1939.

Van Doren, Carl, *Benjamin Franklin*. New York: The Viking Press, 1938.

————, *Secret History of the American Revolution*. New York: The Viking Press, 1941.

Westcott, Allan, editor, *American Sea Power Since 1775*. Philadelphia: J. B. Lippincott Company, 1947.

Willcox, William B., *Portrait of a General: Sir Henry Clinton in the War of Independence*. New York: Alfred A. Knopf, Inc., 1964.

Gratitude also is expressed to Mrs. Thomas Storrow, secretary of the Stonington Historical Society, Stonington, Connecticut, for assistance given in the Fanning research and to the librarians at the Westerly, Rhode Island library.

INDEX